For all my grandchildren, all their cousins and the grandchildren of my friends at Greens.

Wasted Opportunity

The rise and fall of a family business

The story of Edward Green's 'economizer'

ADRIAN BRIDGEWATER
with
STAN JEWSON C.Eng., M.I.MechE., MASME

Acknowledgements

In 1975 Simon Green wrote an unpublished description of the work of Greens and his side of the family row from the time he joined in 1933 without which fuller details could not have been told.

But the history of Greens Economiser Group didn't end until its sale to Senior Engineering in 1983.

During those closing eight years Stan Jewson as Chief Executive and Deputy Chairman played the key role and has been able to bring a much wider perspective to bear on the earlier years, along with factual descriptions of the engineering opportunities and difficulties facing the Company.

I have also been given many anecdotes, ideas and hard facts by my cousins and friends, all of whom have encouraged me to complete and I hope, enhance Simon's early manuscript. These include Simon's grandson David Wallace and his stepdaughter Susan Badcup, Livia Buscall, Georgina Grattan Bellew, Edward Lycett Green, Rupert Lycett Green and Deborah Hinton, and most important of all, my long suffering PA Jayne Ransom.

Adrian Bridgewater
Cambridge 2012

CONNECT
PUBLISHING LIMITED

Published by Connect Publishing
19 High Street, Great Eversden, Cambridge CB23 1HW
Email: adrianbridgewater@gmail.com
ISBN 978-0-9574344-0-0

Contents

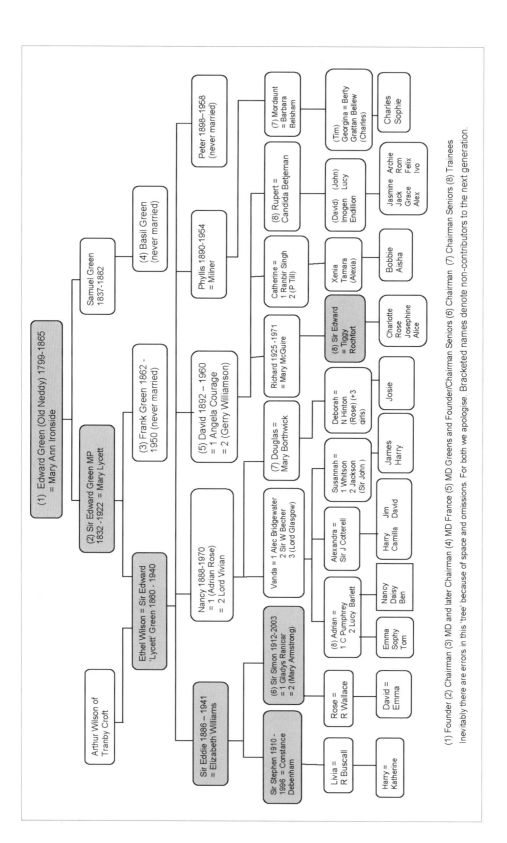

(1) Founder (2) Chairman (3) MD and later Chairman (4) MD France (5) MD Greens and Founder/Chairman Seniors (6) Chairman (7) Chairman Seniors (8) Trainees
Inevitably there are errors in this 'tree' because of space and omissions. For both we apologise. Bracketed names denote non-contributors to the next generation.

Introduction

The founder of the firm, Edward Green 'Old Neddy', sixth son of Thomas Green of Wakefield, was born in 1799 and was apprenticed as a millwright in Wakefield from the age of 14. In 1820 aged 21 he completed his apprenticeship and went into business on his own, aged 22. So, in 1821 E Green and Son was first established with its Kirkgate foundry, supplying steam engines, boilers and other machinery as well as iron bars, rails and piping. But it wasn't until 1843 that Edward Green was able to start experimenting with his 'economizer' having settled a lawsuit and ended a partnership. In 1846 the Manchester Guardian carried an advertisement for a 'Patent Fuel Economizer and Steam Generator'.

Neddy's second son, Edward became a partner in the firm in 1856 aged 27 and on the death of his father in 1865 he took charge.

He was made a Baronet for political services in 1886 and took *'WASTE NOT'* as his family motto. He had been the MP for Wakefield for some 25 years and he was said to have uttered fewer words in the House of Commons than any other member. But in industry he was far better known as head of the second generation of the family which had invented the fuel Economiser in 1845. This was an apparatus which, placed in the path of the flue gases' smoke leaving an industrial boiler, preheated its feed water before the smoke went up the chimney, which saved a lot of money.

Six generations of the Green family served in the business for nearly 140 years, and my first cousin once removed, Simon Green was the last to leave although I and one cousin served as the sixth generation. I don't

Old Neddy 1790-1865

PATENT FUEL ECONOMIZER,

AND

STEAM GENERATOR.

E. GREEN

Solicits the attention of Parties interested in the saving of Fuel used in connection with Steam Engine or other Boilers, to his *New Method of Economizing Fuel, and certain Improvements in retaining and applying Heat for generating Steam and Heating Water*, by which method the Feed Water is first filtered and then heated by the spare heat from the Boiler Flues to boiling Heat, and a considerable quantity of Steam generated, before it enters the Boiler, thereby effecting a saving of about *one-third* of the Fuel ; or *one-third more Steam* is generated with the same Boiler and same quantity of Fuel. The Apparatus can be applied either to New or Old Boilers.

For Plans & Description, see Prospectus, which can be had of

E. GREEN,

ENGINEER, PHŒNIX FOUNDRY,

WAKEFIELD,

WHERE AN APPARATUS MAY BE SEEN AT WORK.

Advertisement from the *'Manchester Guardian'*, 1847

think we made a significant contribution.

Greens produced not much more than a trade brochure to celebrate its 50th year, but shortly after its 100th year a history of the business a book with the title *'Waste Not'* was printed for private publication in 1956. This should have been done far earlier as, of course, those who could have contributed significantly had died and Frank Green, my great uncle who had reached 94, was unwilling to be involved.

Simon Green was determined to try and account for all that had happened during his forty years with the Company and left an incomplete script written in about 1975 which described a damaging family row which split the family against the background of the very great changes and advances in the evolution of electrical power generation which had affected Greens. It was never published

Just when Simon joined the firm in 1933 the row was erupting and was to shake the business to its roots. This row was very much glossed over in *'Waste Not'* as no-one wanted to stir up ill feelings amongst senior staff and family members who were still alive. But today there are many relations on either side of the split to whom the facts about the family row and its impact on the business are of interest. Simon Green was only in his very early twenties at the time and was pitched head first into the row. He was one of the very few people still living who had some first-hand knowledge of what actually took place.

In 1983 Greens was finally taken over by Senior Engineering and selling the Company was the last official duty of the then Deputy Chairman, Stan Jewson. He has helped me to rewrite Simon's script which provided key information but this has been considerably modified and extended in the light of our further enquiries and direct experience. Stan Jewson joined the firm in 1941, just seven years after Simon.

I worked for Greens for two years and in 1957 at a Works Dinner to celebrate the 21st birthday of his daughter Rose, Simon made an unfortunate announcement that I was being 'brought on as a future leader of Greens'. The link between this announcement and the weakening of the firm by Freemasons adds a dimension to a story of wasted opportunities.

Simon was a very gentle and kind man and many years later, in 1988 five years after the Company had been sold to Seniors, he tried to apologise to me for the way I was treated by his Chief Engineer John Rylands who was a leading freemason. He told me to get the truth from Stan Jewson.

There are several lessons in the Greens decline for today's entrepreneurs. In its time Greens was a very important company and working there taught me a great deal which I was able to apply in my own businesses. It also gave me several lifelong friends, including one of Greens most successful foremen, Gordon Betts and an extract from the Appreciation given at his funeral which I attended at Wakefield Cathedral in October 2001 concludes this book.

Edward Green- *circa* 1860

1

The Green Family Connections

In 1942 – in the middle of the war – David Lycett Green invited my mother Vanda to come to Yorkshire to run his house, Bilbrough Manor, his wife Angela having decamped with Ralph Grimthorpe. My father was a regular soldier serving overseas, and his regiment the 5th Royal Inniskillings was based in Catterick. With my sister Alexandra and our nanny Lily March, we joined our first-cousins-once-removed, Richard, Catherine and Rupert and started to get to know the Greens at Bilborough Manor, near York.

David was my Great-uncle and had run the family firm for a while and had then broken away in the row with his Chairman Uncle Frank Green to set up a rival, Senior Economisers. As a small boy I only saw Uncle David as a gallant sailor and knew nothing of his business campaigns. Simon could remember his great grandfather Sir Edward but I can only just remember my great-grandfather Sir Lycett as I was five when he died. But I have quite vivid memories of Sir Lycett's brother, my great Uncle Frank who had fought over the firm with Uncle David, his nephew. Another Great Uncle Basil son of Sir Edward's brother Samuel was never mentioned and I never met him but heard a lot about him when I worked for Greens in France in 1955.

They were all remarkable characters in their different ways. From notes in engineering text books it's obvious that Sir Edward was an inventive, practical engineer and very much the head of the business during its early years between 1860 and 1900. Uncle Frank ran the business from 1890 to 1945 when at the age of 83 he handed it over to Simon. Sir Edward was an entrepreneur who saw the potential of the

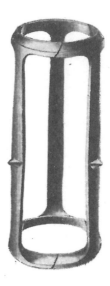

Patent No. 23,900, the Triple Scraper, 1892

Opening ceremony of two new Green's coal fired water tube boilers, 1981. (Stan Jewson second from right)

economiser and spent time, energy and money to develop and patent the key designs – not least a mechanism to scrape soot off the economiser's water tubes - and then exploit them. Frank was a fastidious, tidy-minded executive with a hot temper. He was not an entrepreneur. He told Simon that his father Sir Edward was a very shy man, and that he had great difficulty getting him to take investment decisions for mass production of the economiser. But this may have been unfair as Sir Edward was over 75 at the time and the real problem was that in those days it was neither fashionable nor necessary to retire before death as there was no threat of crippling estate and death duties. So the old man kept control of the purse strings for far too long – as did Frank.

David, like his grandfather Sir Edward, was an ambitious entrepreneur who became frustrated under the control of his uncle Frank, whilst Simon, the reluctant heir to the chair, was clearly uncomfortable in the job, untrained for it and not strong enough to stand up against the forces of Uncle Frank, Freemasonry and advancing technology.

Sir Edward married Mary Lycett in 1859 and they had two sons, Simon's grandfather Edward Lycett, born in 1860, who died in 1940 and Frank born in 1862 who died in 1950. The economiser business was obviously flourishing and Lycett was sent to Harrow, and Frank to Eton. They were very different, the older boy good looking, popular and a brilliant, dashing horseman, whilst Frank was a spotty-faced shy boy with a quick temper. Frank had a tutor in the holidays who couldn't control him and once Frank felled him with his cricket bat. But his older and stronger brother was always able to control him. As young men, they went to stay at the Beverley Arms to hunt with the Holderness. It was not so much the good hunting as the local ladies that attracted them: the brothers had a tremendous fight over who was to claim one of them and Frank was the loser. In retaliation he emptied the hip bath over Lycett's bed. Frank thought he was fighting for the oldest sister Susan, but Edward was after Ethel Wilson, the second daughter of Arthur Wilson of Tranby Court. They later married and had five children including David and my grandmother Nancy. Frank never married.

Edward Green, as a *nouveau riche* proprietor of an engineering business in Wakefield, was not on first sight acceptable to the local gentry, who were adding to their fortunes through their coal mines and were suspicious of this man who had invented a machine to economise on the use of their black diamonds. So it was through the hunting field that the Green family entered County Society. In 1866 Edward bought a fine Elizabethan house, Heath Old Hall, on the outskirts of Wakefield, commissioning Thomas Jeckyll to design 'important' furniture and put

Heath Old Hall, Wakefield

on his pink coat to go out with the Badsworth and Bramham Moor. Further social advance was made by buying land in West Norfolk on the shores of the Wash, where Ken Hill, a Queen Anne Style house, designed by John J Stevenson, was built in 1879 and an outstanding pheasant shoot was created - deliberately close to Sandringham!

His two sons were brought up to be keen on hunting and Lycett's job was to 'ride the family into society' while Frank's was to take on the family business. Lycett went to Cambridge, where he spent most of his time hunting in the winter and playing polo in the summer. Many books on hunting refer to Lycett as being in the first flight of those who 'rode across the country' in his day. After he married he lived on the outskirts of York and for many years was Master of the York & Ainsty. In those days raising a family was considered more important than running a family business, so that was what Lycett, the older brother, had to do.

An impressive memorial to Lycett's pride in his family is the enormous (82 ¼ x 113 ¼ inches) portrait of all his children except Peter - 'Cubbing with the York & Ainsty', painted by C W Furse in the last months before his death aged 34 in 1904. His fee was 630 guineas. This picture was bought for considerably more by my great friend Robert Cooper at the Ken Hill sale in 1999. Lycett also commissioned John Singer Sargent to draw his favourite child, my Grandmother Nancy at about the same time and this picture was left to me as her oldest grandchild. Lycett, like his brother Frank, was a knowledgeable collector of paintings.

In preparation for going into the business Frank was sent to Sulzer Bros in Switzerland, just as I was in 1956, to do practical work on the engineering shop floor. On his return he was put into the E Green and Son head sales office in Manchester, the centre of the rapidly growing textiles industry in which each factory had a Lancashire boiler and a Green's economiser. This is not to say that Frank didn't have plenty of time for leisure and fun. He too was fond of hunting, though he admitted that he never had the same courage as his brother, but he tried to make up for this by buying himself well-bred chestnut horses with long manes and tails. He was also keen on the administration of the hunt and maintaining the goodwill of the local farmers, buying local farms so that fox hunting coverts could be improved.

The two sons obviously financed their operations from the firm's profits. As a young man Lycett went to see the cowboys in America. He telegraphed to his father for money to buy some land and this was abruptly refused with an order to return home before wasting any more money. The site which they were ordered to let go is now part of Chicago!

Simon's father Eddie, the oldest of Ethel and Lycett's five children had been commissioned into the Life Guards, but to get married in his early twenties he had to leave the regiment. Simon's mother, Elizabeth Williams, was the daughter of an impoverished Welsh barrister, originally a journalist, whose wife thought he should upgrade himself by taking silk. Unfortunately he was deaf and couldn't hear opposing counsel or the judge. Elizabeth and her sister were both accomplished musicians but the marriage was not popular with the family and Eddie and his wife were sent to live at Woolgreaves House on the edge of Wakefield and Eddie was made to report to the business for duty. Simon's brother Stephen, was born there in 1910 but it was not long before they moved about nine miles to Darrington Hall, beside one of the most dangerous crossroads on the A1. Letters indicate that Elizabeth was not slow to set up an amusing and popular household but Frank prompted Sir Edward to write and insist that the extravagant expenditure must cease.

Two years later Simon nearly paid his first visit to the Works at Wakefield. July 10th 1912 was a memorable day: King George V and Queen Mary were visiting the Green's Works. Stands were erected in the Works yard so that the wives of employees could see Their Majesties and wave their Union Jacks. A large-scale model of an economiser had

The Royal Visit

been built to explain how they worked. Simon's mother was in the front row of the wives' party but shortly before the King and Queen arrived she 'came over queer' and was rushed back home with the first pains of Simon's impending arrival and he was born in time for lunch the next day.

During his visit, the King is said to have turned to Lycett, who was on a very rare visit to Wakefield, to say that he couldn't quite understand what came out of the chimney sticking up at the end of the economiser model. Lycett replied:

"Foxhunting baronets and champagne, Your Majesty".

Lycett's second son, Uncle David, went to Dartmouth and was later commissioned in the Royal Navy in which he served throughout the 1914-18 war. The third son, Uncle Peter, left school to go straight into the war and got a commission in the Grenadiers. In his first action on the Western Front he was badly wounded and had a leg amputated. In the '50s he used to come down to Treyarnon Bay in Cornwall to stay with my Grandmother, his sister Nancy, to surf and would take off his wooden leg leaving it standing, fully clad in shoe, sock and sock suspender beside our highly embarrassed Nanny March as he hopped into the sea to surf with his admiring great-nephew and great-niece.

Nancy was Lycett's third child with two older brothers David and

Peter and with Simon's father Eddie and Phyllis, grandmother of Georgie Milner, younger than her. Nancy first married Captain Adrian Rose who tragically died from typhoid caught whilst they were on honeymoon in Egypt. She lived as a widow in Belgravia for some years before marrying my Grandfather Lord Vivian of Glynn who was the grandson of General Sir Hussey Vivian who led the last and decisive charge at the Battle of Waterloo (1815). With George Vivian, Nancy had two children, my mother Vanda and Douglas. Before marrying Nancy my grandfather Vivian had had two older children, Tony and Daphne. Daphne married Henry Bath and Alexander Weymouth, Caroline Somerset and Christopher and Valentine Thynne were their children. Nicolas, Victor and Sally Anne were Tony Vivian's children.

When Sir Edward retired from Parliament he left Heath Old Hall, Wakefield and went to live at Nunthorpe Hall, York. Both Frank and his mother hated giving up the fine Elizabethan house for an ugly Victorian mansion. This move also signified Sir Edward's retirement from active business life, though he remained Chairman and continued to attend meetings until his death. Around this time Frank persuaded his father to hand over a considerable proportion of his shares which obviously gave Frank more power in family affairs and he now had to be consulted in all matters of finance. It's clear that Lycett and his family didn't mind his younger brother Frank having more shares but his authority as a holder of the family purse strings was bitterly resented.

After his wife Mary's death, Sir Edward became more of a recluse. As Chairman he continued to attend the Company's Board meetings but spent much of his time living in hotels and became increasingly reluctant to spend money on himself, the family or the business. This meant that Frank had to be consulted more and more so that he could persuade his father to agree to any expenditure.

Lycett's children were growing up fast and three marriages had taken place for each of which financial provision had to come from the Green family, which meant the business, so Frank's support was important. One can see the dilemma – Frank's task was not altogether easy, as his father, being a true Yorkshireman would not spend his 'brass' easily and as he got older was becoming increasingly cautious so Frank felt that his efforts on behalf of his nephews and nieces should have been received with thanks, whereas Lycett's family felt that it was their birthright to have their share and that Frank's efforts were officious.

Frank's favourite. Nancy Lycett who married George Vivian.
Nancy's wedding dress was presented to Lotherton Hall, Nr Leeds.

Nancy's mother Ethel who married 'Sir Lycett' and had five children.

2
The 1914 –1918 War

Towards the end of the 1914-18 War Stephen and Simon spent some time with their great grandfather at Ken Hill and Simon had his introduction to the shooting field. During his walks in the woods around the house he would note all the game he saw and return with pretend game drawn and cut out in cardboard to hang in the nursery 'game larder'.

Of course Eddie was away during the war years but in the summer of 1919 the whole family went to Paris-Plage where they shared a tall grey house with Simon's mother's sister Daisy who had married Charles Nicholl, a London solicitor with Nicholl, Manisty & Few. (later to amalgamate with Withers) They had three daughters, all about the same age as Stephen and Simon and they had a happy summer, rampaging in the sand dunes frightening the French children whilst their parents played golf at Le Touquet. But when September came Stephen was sent to preparatory school at Hawtreys, Westgate on Sea, and Simon went with his mother to the French Riviera where she had rented a villa.

Although Simon was unaware what was going on in the family, these were obviously decisive days and in November when Eddie came out of the army he didn't tell his sons that there was to be a break up of his marriage and that they wouldn't see their mother for several years. Divorce was scandalous and not talked about in front of the children, but plenty went on behind closed doors and it's more than likely that the pressure and control exercised on Simon's mother by her mother- in-law Ethel, which Eddie couldn't combat, caused the split. The fact that Frank, living with his old father was making him control the young couple was resented and led to jealousy. At the same time Elizabeth felt that as she was married to the older son she deserved preference. But in fact it was Nancy, the older daughter and David who were their parents' favourites.

No doubt the war and enforced separation had played their part but Elizabeth resented the fact that they had never been allowed to live their own lives without being told what they might do or not do and when they were told that they must live in an isolated farmhouse on the Ken Hill estate with a limited income, she decided to go, which Simon felt must have been the right decision; she couldn't have existed as a country bumpkin doing good works in the village. She lived abroad for the next twenty years but her scrap books show how she kept contact with her many English theatrical friends including Ivor Novello, the Hulberts, Jack Buchanan and Noel Coward. She spent some years in Italy until her connections with Mussolini's black shirted court became too hot and then went to Portugal where she had a 'husband' who appeared to play no part in matrimonial affairs and was only there so that she could call herself a married woman. After that it was Tangiers and Capri, from where she had to be extricated after the '39 – 45' war.

After his demobilisation in 1919 Eddie didn't return to the family business. Years later Frank told Simon that this was because he was too shy and indecisive to make a 'good man of business' but if Eddie had stayed as a principal in the business Elizabeth would soon have got a pretty shrewd idea of the income which might be available and Sir Edward and Frank thought she would become uncontrollable. So, with the break up of his marriage and dismissal from the firm Eddie took a post-war agricultural course at Oxford followed by a trip round the world before moving into Ken Hill to run the estate.

The Minute Book of E Green & Son actually records that Eddie was replaced as a Director in 1916 by Basil Green who was Frank's cousin and had been living in France looking after continental sales. The executive work at Wakefield was done by Gilbert Tennant described by Frank as *"a brilliant business man and the best salesman I have ever known"*. Tennant no doubt enabled Frank to sit back as Vice-Chairman to his father (now rising 90) and to exercise remote control of the business merely by attending Board Meetings, occasionally visiting the Works and summoning senior staff to see him. Those concerned feared Frank's sharp temper which he used to overcome his shyness. He had his mother's quick brain and a tidy mind in both his business and personal affairs. Above all, he abhorred what he called 'muck and muddle' and on a visit to the Works, when Frank was inspecting the back premises he found fire-fighting equipment stuck away in a corner. So he went to the other end of the Works and lit a fire with some old rubbish. Once the smoke and flames had got a good hold he blew the whistle to call the fire brigade. They duly arrived but with only half the equipment so the Fire Fighting Captain was relieved of his duties.

In his own home Frank was known to go and inspect his kitchen without warning. He would get a maid to wipe the top shelves of the kitchen dresser or the underside of the scullery sink with a cloth and if either showed signs of dirt or grease he would fly into a rage and sweep the pots and pans onto the floor. The kitchen maid would burst into tears and the chef give notice but in those days they could easily be replaced. With an indoor staff of fourteen it was Frank's way of maintaining discipline.

In about 1920 Frank decided to bring his nephews David and Peter into the firm putting them under the eye of Gilbert Tennant. However, in the early summer of 1921 disaster struck when Tennant collapsed and died in the directors' lavatory. This was a great shock to Frank and he recorded in the Minutes "… *the loss not only of a personal friend but also a colleague of outstanding ability whose position it is impossible to fill*". The same meeting went on to offer the post of Managing Director to Basil Green but he didn't wish to surrender his life in Paris and declined. It was then decided to appoint David who was 29 as Managing Director and Peter, who was six years younger, was also put on the Board. As David had very little business experience he needed the assistance of senior staff in the company and therefore the appointments of Kenyon, Sales Manager; Smallwood, Company Secretary & Commercial Manager and Armstrong, Accountant were confirmed. Simultaneously a system of monthly departmental returns and reports to be examined at Board Meetings was put in place.

Rather less than two years later in 1922 Sir Edward died. By his Will one third of the Company's shares went to Frank's brother, the elder son Lycett and two thirds to Frank.

E. Basil Green

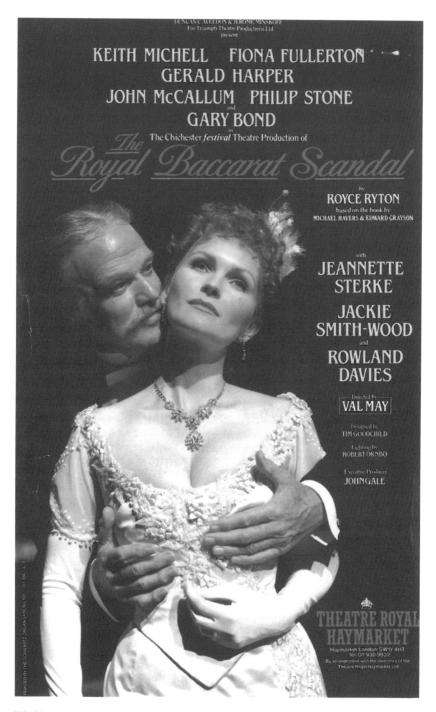

Ethel Lycett Green (Fiona Fullerton) with Sir William Gordon-Cumming (Keith Mitchell)

3
Money and Taboos

Both brothers had now achieved freedom for their personal expenditure. They were both over sixty and perhaps considered they had waited long enough for some extra indulgences before they got too old to enjoy them.

Frank decided to tour Europe in style so built himself a fleet of beautifully appointed caravans comprising a sitting room, two or three bedrooms, a dining room, a kitchen and staff quarters. Each caravan was mounted on a large Leyland chassis. However, when his fleet got to the Channel there was no boat big enough to take it without building a special cargo ship which even Frank considered beyond his purse. So the caravans were sent back to the Yorkshire coast near Filey and offered to impoverished relations for holidays.

Instead, to tour Europe, Frank bought a fleet of eight black Rolls Royces, seven of which were still in his stables in the late forties to be admired longingly by me, his great nephew each time I was taken by my mother to visit him as a prep schoolboy and he tipped me with a crisp white five pound note. Frank gave the eighth Rolls Royce to his chauffeur!

Lycett's indulgence was racing. As a young man he had had some success as an amateur rider; this had been frowned on by Sir Edward but now he could broaden his interest in the 'Sport of Kings'. He became well known on the Northern circuit and many of his horses were home bred at his small stud just outside York.

Not long after their parents' divorce Simon joined his brother Stephen at Hawtreys. They spent all their holidays with their grandparents either at York or at Ken Hill in Norfolk where they were both extremely happy.

The St Ledger house party, Tranby Croft 1891.

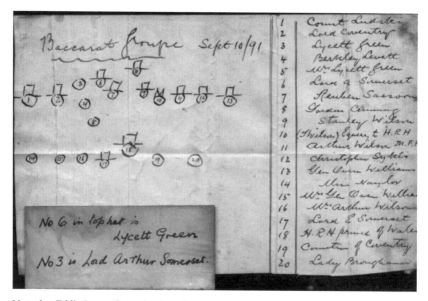

Note that Eddie Lycett Green is given the wrong reference number on the handwritten list.

Their grandmother Ethel looked after them as if they were her own children and they became extremely fond of her. They lived in great comfort in houses full of servants but were firmly disciplined to be punctual and properly turned out, wearing a boiled shirt and stick-up collar with black tie for dinner every night.

Both brothers later described how surprised they were that in their grandfather Sir Lycett's house there was never any mention of the family business or of it being the money provider for the family. It was 'not done' to be connected with industry and if you were, you said nothing about it.

A major 'taboo' was the Baccarat Scandal. Lycett and Ethel were staying at her family home, Tranby Croft where the Prince of Wales was a guest for the Doncaster St Leger race meeting in September 1890. Other guests included the Earl and Countess of Coventry, Lord Edward Somerset, Sir William Gordon-Cumming and Sir Owen Williams. Sir William Gordon-Cumming was accused of cheating in both of the two after dinner games of Baccarat played on successive nights. Five of the players told Lord Coventry what they had witnessed on both nights and he in turn interviewed Gordon-Cumming who emphatically denied the accusation and begged to see the Prince of Wales, which he did later in the evening. The upshot of night-long discussions was that Gordon-Cumming agreed and signed a document approved by the five witnesses and the Prince, which was tantamount to a confession. Gordon Cumming later claimed that he only did this under extreme pressure and to avoid a terrible scandal in which the Prince would be involved. The gist of the document was that in consideration of the promise of all the other players never to speak about the affair, Gordon-Cumming would never play cards again in his life. But, inevitably the accusation of cheating soon got around the London drawing rooms and clubs and Gordon-Cumming had no alternative but to bring an action against his accusers for slander. But he lost the case and the wretched man was forced to leave the country in disgrace.

Almost exactly a hundred years later a play, *The Royal Baccarat Scandal*, opened at the Theatre Royal, Haymarket based on a book written by Edward Grayson and Michael Havers. The latter later became Attorney General in Margaret Thatcher's Government. At lunch at the Garrick Club, during the week the play opened, Havers leant across the centre table to ask me if I thought he had been too hard on my kinsman young Lycett Green. In the play Havers' storyline was that Lycett was young and nouveau-riche and had little or no experience of how to behave in the echelons of high society. More significantly Havers had characterised Lycett Green as determined to destroy Gordon-Cumming because he had been having an affair with his wife Ethel and used the 'confession' document as a device to do so. Havers was worried that the family might have taken offence but thought that Lycett had anyway stirred the issue up and stupidly made so much fuss that the disastrous document had had to be organised and signed (Lycett was 30 years old at the time). So this could have been the reason why the subject of the case was taboo at Ken Hill!

Books and articles about the case over the next 50 years lean towards the feeling that the Judge's summing up was inadequate and that an injustice was done, although the Green family later received a letter from a Somerset landowner congratulating the family for seeing off a rogue who was a known cheat at cards.

Another taboo was money. Sons and grandsons were not expected to enquire about finance, or bother unduly about careers but the industrial world was first brought to Simon's notice by the General Strike in 1926. He had not been at Eton very long and considered it a great injustice that his brother and he were sent up to London before the end of the holidays as there would be no trains after that. Stephen was older and brighter than Simon and had strong views about the injustice which he felt the workers were suffering. This influenced his very left wing political opinions over the next decade and was not popular in the family. Stephen was convinced that when the workers took over, the whole Ken Hill estate would be turned into allotments.

The
Royal Baccarat
Scandal

A play by
Royce Ryton

Based on the book by
Michael Havers and Edward Grayson

Samuel French Ltd

4
The Early Tensions

Stephen and his first cousin Mordaunt Milner, whose mother was Great Aunt Phyllis Lycett Green, had been earmarked to follow as the next generation to run the firm. However, Stephen had become a barrister and Mordaunt, who had been selected as he had gone to Oundle, the school for budding engineers, hated engineering and had a passion for racing. He embarked on his engineering training at Babcock & Wilcox but when he was caught running a betting shop on the workshop floor with a boiler drum as his office, he hurried off to his great uncle Frank to explain that he felt quite unsuited to a life in economisers.

When Stephen had made his career decision to become a lawyer Simon was in his last six months at Eton and his housemaster summoned him because his father had asked whether his mathematical standard was high enough to take an engineering degree. At this stage it had been assumed that Simon would become a farmer or go into the Army but he had gained the minimum number of credits in School Certificate for exemption from the Cambridge Entrance Examination and had specialised in History and Greek which he considered the least arduous subjects. He had only taken a credit in Ordinary Mathematics. So his tutor advised that it was inappropriate for him to pursue engineering. As an alternative, a modern language qualification was suggested so he left Eton a term early and went off to Berlin for the summer to learn German. Twelve months later Hitler was firmly in power and there was little immediate chance of perfecting his German.

During his first term at Magdalene, Cambridge Simon was told by his father that there was a definite prospect of going into the business if

Frank Green. The family ordered him
to get rid of his French 'boyfriend'!

he wanted, but that he must go and see his great uncle Frank who was
Chairman and was living on the edge of Exmoor. Every other young
member of the family had seen Frank before him and Simon was warned
that he would be 'put through the course', which meant being given
instructions on how to behave himself from morning to night. One had
to conform to the regular hours of the house and always be punctual.
There was hunting on at least four days each week and Frank inspected
and criticised everyone's hunting clothes. The buttons of breeches had
to be in exactly the right position with the top one 'in the hole that God
made for it', the other running straight down the shin bone. Boots had to
be exactly the right height and, if new, at least 1 ½" allowed for dropping.
Tying the stock meant special attendance in Frank's bedroom. Invariably
a stock provided by the trade, was *'the wrong shape and was only for
actors and photographers' models'*. One was then given a specially
folded and partially starched piece of linen to put round ones neck and
ordered to follow Frank as he tied his own stock. At the end of his visit
Simon was sent to Frank's London tailors to be properly turned out,
entirely at Frank's expense.

Frank told Simon that if he took a degree at Cambridge he would be
taken into the business. It didn't matter what subject he read because
Frank took the view that a degree was proof that the brain functioned, but
he also made it clear that he would like to see more of Simon during his

years at Cambridge and so Simon embarked on his course to join the Company, visiting Frank very regularly.

But there was more than his future career to think about. One Gladys Ranicar, an attractive woman who was considerably older than Simon was living at Ashwick in an ill-defined role thought by the family to be Frank's *'land girl'*. Some said that Frank had adopted her; she was easily young enough to be his daughter. But others were pretty sure that Frank used her to cover up his sexual preference for young men and presented Gladys as his 'girlfriend'. Judging by his obsessively perfect suits, beautiful handmade shirts and bow ties and impeccable houses, coupled with his fiery temper, Frank certainly didn't match the stereotype of either a country gentleman or a Yorkshire industrialist. Simon's step-daughter further confirmed this, telling me that the family ordered Frank to get rid of his young French 'boy friend'.

But Frank was very fond of Gladys and was worried about how the family would treat her after his death. Georgina Grattan Bellew told me that her father Mordaunt Milner who was Frank's first choice as a successor to take over the business from him was offered the job by Frank – but on the condition that he married Gladys. Mordaunt turned down this proposition and only then did Frank make the same offer with same condition to Simon. Luckily, Simon had become quite keen on Gladys on his numerous visits and wrote that he was surprised and pleased by the proposition. In 1935 they married. Simon was 23 and Gladys was over 40. They had one child, Rosie who married Ronnie Wallace and they had one son, David.

It was during Simon's three years at Cambridge that the row between Frank and David about how the firm should be managed intensified and the family became more and more estranged from Frank. So Frank brought Gladys and Simon into the on-going discussions and they became closely aware of the background to this damaging situation. Stan Jewson confirms that in offering Simon the prospect of Chairmanship of the firm to succeed him, Frank insisted that Simon break all relations with his entire family, except his father who was unwell.

Meanwhile 1926 had been a bad year for Frank with a fall from his horse fracturing his elbow, double pneumonia and an attack of typhoid. All this gave him good reason to plan his departure from Yorkshire. He bought Ashwick, a Victorian villa five miles from Dulverton on the edge of Exmoor and made it comfortable, living in style with ten indoor servants, two or three gardeners and a stable-full of horses. Particularly regular visitors were his two nieces, Nancy and Phyllis, and their families. Frank had also bought a long lease of a house in London at 186

Frank Green with his staff outside Treasurer's House

Ebury Street where again a free bed and lodging was always on offer. A few doors away his nephew Peter had acquired 162 Ebury Street.

Frank had also spent a small fortune restoring Treasurer's House, York where he had lived in great style for several years but he left the house and gave it complete with contents to the National Trust. His Yorkshire hunting acres were put into the 'Ainsty Trust' and David was made the beneficiary with power to appoint to his children. This was mostly farm land on the West side of York which had been acquired by purchasing farms where the occupants were being difficult about the activities of the York and Ainsty Hunt.

So it was generally considered that with his disposal of his Yorkshire properties Frank had finally retired to live in the West of England. However, for too long he had been exercising remote control of the business and as he still retained a majority interest he thought it right to remain Chairman. Perhaps it was unfortunate that he didn't attend Board meetings; in fact, the Minute Book records that after his father's death he only attended a Board meeting about twice a year, so he was out of touch with the current events and technical changes which were affecting the business. But he had a good brain and used it to ask pertinent questions and to insist on detailed replies which no doubt annoyed those who were managing the business and probably thought they had better things to do. Frank felt that with the help of Gilbert Tennant he had built up a first rate way to organise and control, which he demanded should be maintained by David.

In 1924 David was married to Angela Courage with a summer wedding at Kirkby Fleetham. He was the popular uncle, always ready for a bit of fun with his nephews and nieces. The business in Wakefield and hunting in the Winter kept him tied to Yorkshire and his keenness for hunting was shared by Angela .

It's clear that Frank encouraged David to hunt as much as possible but it was hunting that caused the first family tensions. David went down to Ashwick to tell Frank that the York & Ainsty Committee had invited him to be Master in the next season. He felt sure that his uncle would be delighted to hear that he was being asked to follow in his father's footsteps. But Frank, although acknowledging the honour of the Committee's invitation, counselled that it would be impossible to be both Master of Hounds and Managing Director of E Green & Son at the same time and that therefore the offer should be declined. But David had already told the Committee he would take the Hounds and couldn't go back on his word. This infuriated Frank and although he didn't insist that David refuse the Mastership he never forgave him for taking his decision without first seeking his advice.

Most unfortunately whilst the row between Frank and David was building up, significant technical changes were taking place which would be bound to affect Green's business. The old traditional economiser design was being challenged by the development of stronger materials to withstand the increasing working pressures of larger steam generating plants. Electricity demand was growing fast and to meet this demand larger sized boilers were being designed and installed. There was an expanding market for power stations which in those days were mostly owned by municipal corporations; in addition electric power companies were increasing in numbers and in size, both at home and overseas.

All this meant that as factories could now buy electric power, in-plant steam generation of electricity declined. This reduced the number of customers for Green's economisers, though not the volume of business, as generating capacity was still increasing. Also there were still individual industrial demands for fuel economisers, particularly in factories which required hot water or steam for their production processing rather than for generating electricity. These ranged from laundries to paper mills.

To meet the new technical changes Greens developed cast iron tubes with an expanded surface of fins or gills. Gilled tubes had first appeared as potential competition on the Continent, but the mechanical strength of steel tubes was needed to meet the rising operating pressure of the new and bigger boilers. The boilermakers themselves were starting to offer their own steel tube economisers and this meant competition for Greens, which was beginning to look serious, although corrosion due to low feed water temperatures shortened the working life of the steel tubing.

In 1927 the Power Speciality Company, a subsidiary of Foster Wheeler Corporation, USA, was operating in the UK selling boiler plant design. Its success was limited as, being owned by an American Boiler Company, the British counterparts were not anxious to help them. However, in 1928 Greens agreed to buy the Patents for the Foster Economiser. In brief, the main feature was cast iron sleeves with gills, shrunk onto steel tubes to give them internal strength and protection from corrosion. There were fourteen years of the Patent still to run but Greens were still selling this Foster tube fifty years later. It was an extremely good buy without which they would not have been able to stay in the new power station market. But as with most new engineering projects there were teething problems as well as keen competition in the old economiser business which traditionally Greens would have seen off. But there was fierce opposition.

Reduced profits were obviously a worry to Frank and his questions to Wakefield intensified. When Frank had been touring Austria he had been taken ill and stayed on into the winter at Semmering and with nothing much better to do, he sent for his old henchmen, Harry Kenyon who had been Gilbert Tennant's right hand man in the Sales Department and Smallwood, the Company Secretary, who in his spare time also kept the records of Frank's private finance.

This period was the beginning of the real trouble and became known as 'Simmerings from Semmering'. Frank maintained that he wrote many letters to David expressing not only concern about financial results in the monthly reports but also concern that in the replies from Wakefield he noticed a distinct tone and style that he knew was not David's although David signed them. He, therefore, put pressure on Kenyon and Smallwood to find out what was going on. They both had to admit that their own authority as members of the Board of Control was being undermined. Fewer and less meaningful meetings were being held. Early in 1928 the Board of Control meeting had been reduced to reports rather than executive management meetings. Frank certainly didn't like this. Smallwood reported that his position as Secretary of the Company was being undermined as Armstrong, the Accountant, whose appointment he had recommended, was no longer reporting to him but went straight to the Managing Director, David. Similarly, Kenyon had to admit that he was no longer fully in charge of sales.

The purchase of the Foster Economiser Patents had brought with it the Chief Salesman of the Power Speciality Company, Dundas Heenan. With David he had been made an executive director of Green's new subsidiary company Eco Power with headquarters in London.

It was now becoming clear to Frank that the business was no longer being run by his nephew David under the guidance of his Board of Control and Departmental Heads, but by Armstrong the Accountant. On the other hand David who was not at Wakefield every day of the week, needed someone to be his number two. No doubt he thought Armstrong had the strongest personality. The older Board of Control members were adequate, hardworking individuals, capable in their own departments, but none showed the higher potential of Armstrong who proved this in later years, becoming a determined and ruthless competitor. He liked to have his own way and showed a quick temper if he was denied. Perhaps anyone in David's position would have made the same choice but Frank was offended that David never consulted him or asked for help with management. Not only had Frank put David in the driving seat but also he had given him a substantial number of shares, helped to furnish his house when he married, and given him a large acreage of land. He felt he deserved to be consulted and kept in touch. The problem of course was Frank himself, old, isolated in the West country and still wanting to be in control. David had exciting new ideas and was being frustrated by Frank's remote control of both the family's finances and its firm.

Frank had made David's brother Peter a Director, giving him some shares and suggesting that it would only be necessary to be in Wakefield about half-time. Peter lived with his parents Lycett and Ethel in York and commuted to Wakefield by train. He used a small office on the top floor of the Executive block, periodically sending for figures and signing cheques, but he spent most of his time reading. He was fond of music and a connoisseur of pictures and porcelain. It annoyed Frank that Peter interpreted half-time working as going to Wakefield for a week when it suited him and absenting himself for long periods in his London House where he kept up his art pursuits. As with David, Frank felt that he had done a great deal for Peter and later in the row it came as a shock when Peter took his brother David's side and supported Armstrong. Frank had hoped that Peter would take a more detached view, particularly as he was clever, investing wisely in stocks and shares and in his collections of pictures and porcelain. Peter was also very close to his mother Ethel who had always resented Frank's hold on the family finances, both before and after Sir Edward's death.

By 1929 adverse trade conditions had set in. 1929-32 had shown a decline in profits which, by 1932, had begun to look serious. The general slump in trade had caught up with the capital goods industry and caused a reduction in turnover and the situation worried Frank and stirred him to get into close touch. Because of the growing animosity between him and his nephews and his reluctance to be away from Somerset, he didn't want to attend regular Board meetings himself. Instead, he made Basil Green come over from Paris for meetings and in March 1932 Basil moved a Board resolution that an independent adviser be appointed to investigate and report on overheads and working expenses. Frank also got R James, senior partner in the family solicitors, Darley Cumberland & Co., onto the Board and charged him with bringing his messages to the Board meetings. On one occasion James put fifteen questions from Frank to the meeting for which minuted answers were required. These meetings were obviously annoying for David and Peter.

Sir Lycett seated and Ethel standing, with the Wilson family

5
The 'Senior' Break Away: 1933

During this period my Grandmother Nancy Vivian was becoming more and more involved as a link between Frank and his nephews, her brothers. She had always kept in close touch with him, both at Ashfield on Exmoor, which was en route to her Cornish home Glynn and in London. During the Summer when my mother Vanda was coming out she often stayed in Frank's Ebury Street house and as Peter also had a house in Ebury Street it was simple to go from one to the other bearing olive branches. At one stage it looked as if this might be successful and there was one particular 'peace party' which confirmed that some of the cash reserves should be taken out of the Company. In 1933 there was a reconstruction of the Company and nearly a million pounds was distributed to the shareholders, leaving 536,000 £1 shares in the business.

A 51% majority still remained in Frank's hands and the remainder was held by Lycett and his children, of whom David and Peter were the largest holders, having received shares from Sir Edward when they first joined the Company in the early twenties and subsequently from Frank in 1930, and further shares from their father after the 1933 distribution. It was generally felt that this reconstruction would make Frank financially much less dependent on the business and that he would therefore stop interfering with policy and executive management.

But before giving up his Chairmanship Frank was determined to reduce the executive power of David's 'manager', Armstrong. The independent Report on the business had just been concluded by Peat, Marwick & Mitchell. Whilst it went into considerable detail about overhead expenditure and contained numerous recommendations about economies it also made special reference to management. No doubt Frank had expressed his personal misgivings about Armstrong's position to the senior partner compiling the report, but the Report made no adverse comment about his competence, advising that a General Manager be appointed to assist David.

Frank attended the Board Meeting in person on 23rd June at which Harold Livsey was appointed General Manager. As Chairman, Frank had the power to define Livsey's duties. The object was to strip Armstrong of many of the powers he had been given by David, or had assumed and force him to revert to the position of Accountant.

Livsey who had been found by Sir Leonard Coates, a partner of Blackburn, Coates & Co, Green's auditors, was in his late fifties and had previously been engaged in a difficult reconstruction of the Leeds engineering firm James Fowler & Co. In Wakefield he found his position far from easy as his appointment was highly resented by Armstrong and David wasn't cooperative. When Stan Jewson started working for Greens in the Drawing Office in 1941 Livsey, who was still in the saddle, was known as the Hatchet Man. He clearly ran a very tight ship and had had to let a lot of people go to reduce overheads

Frank suggested that the animosity, which had been foreseen, could be overcome if David took an extended world business trip, leaving Livsey to sort out his relationship with Armstrong. This seemed a reasonable solution as the Company had many overseas branch offices and agents who had not been visited by a Green for ages. There was a subsidiary company in the USA and Greens had direct sales representatives with good markets in South America, South Africa, India, Australia, China and Japan. In those days, with travel by sea, it would have taken a good year. However, David was determined not to go and the atmosphere at Wakefield continued to get more difficult. David would not demote Armstrong as had been demanded by the Board. Even David's wife Angela got involved, telephoning Ashwick to speak to Gladys in a last attempt to find some compromise, but this concluded with Frank's brief message that the only solution was for Armstrong to leave the Company. There was stalemate, all boiling down to the power of one man - Frank. Whether he was right or wrong about Armstrong he felt that he should have been consulted and that David should have been more tractable. He was also surprised that none of the family ever questioned his opposition to Armstrong. Simon wrote

'if the family had questioned Frank', they might have heard about his hunch about a sinister plot to break away'.

It's just possible that David had not realised that he had been manoeuvred into a position from which it would be impossible to withdraw, without letting Armstrong down.

After Peter returned from his long summer vacation he decided to resign from the Board thus intimating to Frank that he couldn't agree with the proposals for Armstrong's demotion and that if they went ahead the Company would be left without effective management or Directors. In the middle of October David told Livsey that he intended to leave the Company and start a rival business, taking all the best men with him and subsequently all the trade of the Company. In fact Peter's resignation left the door wide open for Frank's next move. He was not the sort of man to be frightened by David's threats and at the Board meeting on November 28th 1933 it was proposed that the office of Managing Director be declared vacant. As David was unable to vote on this proposal the resolution was carried without a dissenting voice.

David left the Company and three weeks' later Senior Economisers Limited was a registered and active company in competition with Greens.

E.A. Lycett Green   Frank Green   F.D. Lycett Green
(Eddie)   Sir Edward Green   (Peter)
1912

6
Senior Engineering Up and Running 1934-36

It was obvious that considerable thought had gone into setting up the break-away firm. The threat of leaving with some of Green's best men had been more than just words and it quickly became clear that many of the up and coming staff, particularly young technical engineers and draughtsmen, had been approached before David departed with Armstrong. The latter was the first to go, joined at the same time by Dundas Heenan, who had been planning his new Sales set up under the cover of Green's subsidiary company Eco Power. In particular he had been to the Green's Manchester Office and made approaches to Walter Parker who had spent his life working there and was on the point of retiring. It was surprising that Heenan could have thought he might persuade Parker to join as he was greatly respected by Green's many customers in the Lancashire cotton industry. Green's headquarters had originally been in Manchester, its most prolific source of orders, and if Parker and his two assistants had gone over to Seniors it would have been a serious blow. Parker had succeeded his own father who had also had a lifetime of service and regarded himself as part of the Greens family business. He had always liked and respected David as he was a Green. So he was upset by the split but remained loyal and made a special journey to see Frank and tell him so. Frank summoned Simon to this meeting as he wanted Parker to see that another generation of Greens was coming along and that he wasn't going to give in to Seniors who were now known as 'the reds'.

Obviously these were difficult days for Green's staff and though very few jumped ship, many must have been in a dilemma when approached.

Early on Armstrong was spreading propaganda and his confident prediction that within six months of the formation of Seniors old Frank would be forced to give in and that therefore those who joined Seniors, the new company, would be highest on its promotion ladder.

In his position as effective deputy managing director of Greens, Armstrong had been able to give instructions to all the staff which he could expect to be carried out without question and he had sent for all the standard parts drawings and compendia with prices, all to be forwarded to Eco Power, where they were copied before return to Wakefield.

The Sales side of the new company was quickly established and Heenan, as the ex super salesman of Eco Power, was able to go round all the main customers, particularly in the new high pressure economiser market, explaining the superiority of Seniors' new designs and that Seniors had been forced to break away and start a new business as Greens would not accept such innovation.

At first there was speculation about which designs Seniors would adopt and whether they would copy the vertical tube economiser which was still based on the original invention. To manufacture this to compete with Greens' vertical tube economiser would have required heavy investment in specialised machinery, so not surprisingly, the more modern horizontal gilled tube design was adopted. The extended surface on gilled tubes allowed more heating surface space to be concentrated on a smaller number of tubes than on plain tubes without gills so that this newer type of economiser occupied less space and for new installations was cheaper. Greens were also selling the Fosters design with round gills on round tubes but Seniors came up with a design which was new to the British market. Here again it was apparent that some groundwork had been done before the break away of the 'reds'. The H-tube patented design had been acquired from one of Green's competitors in France, Coneconomiseur, owned by the Hubert family. The tubes for this economiser had gills in the shape of an 'H' with the tubes arranged in parallel. These presented a very effective straight gas passage which could be cleaned reasonably easily with steam blowers or, when out of commission, by rodding. For the higher pressure boilers – at that time above 400 lbs per square inch – steel tubes were necessary, and Seniors incorporated an 'H' cast iron sleeve as an alternative to Green's Foster Economiser with round sleeves. This they called the Heenan – Twin Tube and a licence for this high pressure type was swapped with Conecomoniseur for their cast-iron tube design.

Frank Green immediately started asking the Greens French Company about the reputation and performance of these economisers, where they were installed in France and also why the French Company had not informed Wakefield about them. Basil Green, who received 'a proper ticking off' from the Chairman, replied that it was known and he thought it had been reported to Wakefield but in any case it was an inferior design. This was certainly not true, and in a very short time Scurr, who had been Green's Chief Sales representative in France, left to join Seniors. No doubt he had been engaged in the negotiations for the acquisition of the 'H' design by Seniors.

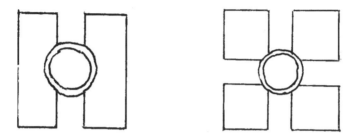

Seniors' original 'H' design (left) and Green's later spot-welded tube

It was thought that manufacture might be difficult for Seniors. But here again there was evidence that preliminary planning must have been well on its way when it was announced that Seniors had a manufacturing agreement with International Combustion Ltd at Derby. The Managing Director of this company was George Usher – later to be knighted during the war years for his service to the Ministry of Supply in tank production.

George Usher's involvement may have been the main reason why the Greens family row could not be resolved as one might have expected by the family themselves. After all, Frank was over seventy when the break came and his so called interference could not have lasted much longer. Moreover the expectation that he would not wish to interfere so much when he got a substantial sum of money out of the business by the 1933 distribution had never been given a proper chance to materialise. Exactly when a scheme which had been planned by Usher, Heenan and Armstrong was presented to David is not known. It obviously had its attractions from a financial point of view as well as offering a way to beat his difficult old uncle. But when the final decision came it was too late for David to withdraw even if he wanted and he probably thought that Frank would find the old management at Wakefield so inefficient that he would compromise and give in.

In the early days prior to the 1914-18 war George Usher had been employed as office boy in Green's German branch office in Cologne.

About half a dozen people were employed dealing mainly with sales, installation and service. Sales representatives didn't have cars in those days but travelled mostly by train and bus. However, Greens were quite forward looking in having a motorbike. Once, when Frank was visiting Cologne all the staff had to be present for examination and account of their duties; evidently Frank was dissatisfied with the sales coming from this office and after soundly rebuking the sales representatives he announced that the most effective person appeared to be the office boy Usher and he should be given the motorbike and sent out selling.

That young George Usher should have shown this early eagerness and ability to get on was no surprise to those who later saw his great success in business. He was soon promoted and sent to the USA as a salesman for the Green Fuel Economiser Corporation which had been established as a separate subsidiary company in 1904. In the early days vertical economisers had sold well and the volume of business had justified setting up a manufacturing company at Beacon, which lay on the east side of the Hudson river in New York State. With the war in Europe and the parent company's concentration on munitions the American subsidiary company was being neglected. Also there were manufacturing competitors in the United States: the Sturtevant Engineering Company in Boston had virtually copied the vertical economiser. This competition, coupled with the stagnation of economiser design, prompted the eager Usher to look for other forms of expansion. He had made friends with a man named Hagen who was an up and coming mechanical draft fan engineer. He demonstrated to Usher that he had new designs which would Improve the efficiency of fan performance and he was anxious to join a company which would develop this. Usher agreed to take on Hagen but his decision was not well received by the President of Green Fuel Economizer Inc, a Mr Nield, partner in the firm of auditors –Davies & Davies. Usher therefore travelled to England to see Frank Green and report that he had engaged a first class fan engineer to develop a new product line for Greens. In the meantime, Nield had communicated to Frank that Usher was on his way and that he would resign as President if Green Fuel Economizer Inc continued to employ Usher. Consequently on arrival in England Usher was smartly told to get back to the USA to sell economisers and not to bother about fans. Usher, being reluctant to accept this decision, not least as he had already given his word to engage Hagen, refused to do so. Consequently he was given the sack.

For several years Usher doesn't seem to have crossed Green's path but when he became Managing Director of International Combustion

Ltd he was running a company which was potentially one of Green's best customers for economisers. He was thus very well placed to get his own back on Frank for sacking him.

Ironically Usher had been right. Hagen proved to be a brilliant engineer introducing the air-foil design which became the basis for high efficiency fans all over the world. However not many years later Green Fuel Economizer Inc did enter the Fan market and eventually fans became their main product but they would have got going much more quickly and successfully if they had gone ahead with Usher's recommendation to employ Hagen.

Colonel Simon Greenm T.D, D.L, Chairman and Managing Director.

Designed by John J Stevenson, Ken Hill was built for Sir Edward in 1879 as a shooting lodge.

When Sir Steven's will was opened after his death in 1996 it was found that instead of leaving Ken Hill to his older grandson Harry who had already taken possession of the estates including Eaton Farm, the main house had been left to David Lycett Green's grandson - the 'new' Sir Edward. Without its supporting farmland there was no question of being able to retain the house which was sold with just 5 acres of grounds. The contents were sold in 1999.

7
The Senior Strategy and a Possible Reconciliation

International Combustion (ICL) had become one of the leading British boilermakers during the war years. With Usher under the chairmanship of George Taylor they were backed by an energetic board of directors, several of whom were also directors of important international undertakings who were good potential customers for ICL and they built up a successful business with additional assistance from Combustion Engineering, USA. They incorporated the 'L' type underfeed stoker which was one of the most popular methods of firing boilers at that time and were forerunners in the development of pulverised fuel firing in the UK. They were second only to Babcock & Wilcox who had the largest share of the business which came under the wing of the Water Tube Boilermakers Association. The other members were John Thompson WTB, Clarke Chapman, Simon Carves and Yarrow. All of these were customers of Greens and potential customers of the new Senior Economiser Ltd who had chosen this name as they claimed to be the senior branch of the Green family of whom David's father, Lycett, was the head.

As part of his job as Managing Director of Greens David had got to know all these boilermakers and so he came in direct touch with Usher. Also by chance Dundas Heenan lived in Kings Langley, very close to George Usher's house, so here again was an opportunity for meetings and connivance away from the places where one might be seen.

When Usher had originally influenced the sale of the Foster Economiser Patent to Greens who had formed Eco Power he, with Heenan and Armstrong, had an ulterior motive. When the sales initiative of Greens was taken away from Wakefield and transferred to Eco Power in London under Heenan, Wakefield was subjugated to a purely manufacturing role. Eco Power could then have been hived off from the rest of Greens and exploited as a company in its own right. But Frank Green had been informed by Kenyon and Smallwood of their fears and he put a stop to this. But it gave Usher his great opportunity to get his own back on Frank. He was well aware of the conflicts brewing up in the management of the Green business and because he was still chippy about being sacked by Frank, he was keen to add fuel to the fire by offering his assistance to David if he broke away to start a new company.

In the years between the wars employees began to be able to make money by acquiring shares in new companies in which they were employed or had influence. Having built them up they could profit by floating them in stock market listings. But with a tax burden of over 90% this was unhappily becoming difficult. At Senior Economisers Usher, Armstrong and some of their colleagues were able to acquire shares on the ground floor and by assisting Seniors with manufacture, making them sole suppliers of economisers for International Combustion Boilers, Usher was of the greatest possible help in getting Seniors going. If the war had not intervened it could well have happened earlier but shortly after the war Senior Economisers Ltd became listed as a public company with a handsome capital profit to those who had got in at the start.

Simon wrote:

> 'One can only admire those who had the wit and ability to exploit the opportunities that they themselves had created. But one must also question the behaviour of Usher and Armstrong. Were they mere opportunists planning to exploit David's frustration with Frank? It was never possible to find out what David really thought and there is no clue as to whether he divulged or discussed his views with members of the family. Perhaps he didn't really know what was going on but he must surely have believed that Frank would give in. Either way David must have thought that the time had come for the Greens family business to go public which would have been to his own financial advantage as well as to other family shareholders'.

It is clear that Usher made the breakaway of Seniors a viable proposition and made a large profit in the process, so the big question is whether David was in cahoots with Usher or whether Usher made him an offer he couldn't refuse. It's also self-evident that Frank had stayed on far too long as Chairman and was obstructing Green's progress to such an extent that for David to have been plotting to force Frank to resign cannot be judged unreasonable.

Although plans were well laid for the formation of Seniors it's never easy to start a new business. Not unexpectedly, Seniors arrival on the scene caused a good deal of speculation in the Water Tube Boilermakers Association which had been formed for the rationalisation of manufacture. Some form of price control and quotas was inevitable and arguably helped to build up a strong and thriving industry with large export markets throughout the world.

Babcock & Wilcox were the largest of the boilermakers, followed by International Combustion then John Thompson Water Tube Boilermakers. Both Babcocks and Thompsons had been manufacturing their own economisers for some of the new high pressure boiler installations, but had also been placing a lot of business with Greens. For more or less standard design of industrial boilers the inclusion of a Green's economiser was automatic.

Babcock's were particularly concerned that the close connection of Seniors with International Combustion would disrupt the industry. Both Greens and Seniors were busy rushing round their important customers with Greens seeking to preserve their connection and Seniors trying to break in as new suppliers.

Babcock's Managing Director McKinstry was wooed by David and this was countered by Frank who made what was for him a special visit. McKinstry made it plain that he would like to see some settlement if it were at all possible. Frank obviously made an impression on McKinstry with his assurance that he wished to continue working closely with Babcock and agreed to see what could be done but in a subsequent memorandum to Livsey who had been deputed to be Green's main link with McKinstry for the immediate future, Frank wrote –

'There are people you cannot make an agreement with. David would never forgive me pressing on Green's Board that his ability was not suited for the post he occupied as Managing Director. However much he was out of the business he would help anyone to ruin me if he could. The other is Usher who, a long time ago, we did not retain in our employ in the USA. Instead of Usher being grateful to me for the good advice I gave him which I always think enabled him to get his present position, took it very badly and I am told he would do anything to annoy me. He has grown no wiser. He should know by now it is difficult to annoy a man of 72 – at that age one does not care and unless there is some great flight from the pound, I have sufficient apart from business for my modest wants. You could never make an

agreement with Mr U as regards myself".

To outsiders the position did look rather absurd. Seniors shareholders were backing a new company which was trying to defeat Greens and in doing so were likely to reduce Green's profits when a large majority of Senior's shareholders still had a 49% holding in Greens. Were they likely to gain on the swings what they would lose on the roundabouts? Surely Frank would give in or at least come to some agreement that would suit David. People on both sides, Greens and Seniors, were promoting negotiation and McKinstry continued to be in the forefront.

However negotiations were rudely interrupted on April 28th 1934 when David issued a Writ in the High Court of Justice King's Bench Division. The short title and reference to the record is *David Cecil Lycett Green v E Green & Son Ltd 1934 G No 771*, claiming damages for wrongful dismissal from his employment as Managing Director. The Statement of Claim in the action was delivered on April 30th and the sum of £2,333-6-8d was claimed as damages, being eight months' remuneration. It can't have been the cash damages that David was after but rather to annoy Frank into making a move. He would not like the publicity of going to Court. For maximum publicity David had briefed Patrick Hastings so Frank employed another 'star' QC, Norman Birkett, for the defence. Both were top names at that time. During the preparation of the defence there was speculation about whether Frank would appear as a witness but the day before the case was due in court Birkett insisted on an interview with Frank. Livsey and Simon accompanied Frank to Birkett's chambers. No doubt he wanted to sum up his client and his likely behaviour as a witness. Birkett briefly outlined the course he thought he would take and then turned to Frank and said, as reported by Simon:-

> *"I think we will win but I shall have to pull out all the stops and in particular the evidence regarding the removal and photography of technical detail and price lists. I believe that this evidence could well lead to criminal proceedings being taken against Armstrong and that it would be unavoidable for your nephew to be coupled in such a suit. I feel I must bring this to your notice in case you did not want proceedings against your nephew to go so far".*

Frank replied that he felt there was little he could do about it. The Company's honour was at stake. After all David was bringing the case against the Company and if he was foolish enough to get himself otherwise embroiled in so doing it was up to him to withdraw. So it was decided to stand firm and Frank and his team were asked to return to Birkett's chambers at 9.30 the next morning for final preparation before moving across to the law courts.

Frank was staying at the Ritz with Gladys and Simon and the case had been the main topic of conversation for some weeks, Gladys always maintaining that David would not go to Court. On the morning of the case, Gladys came to the steps of the hotel to see Frank and Simon off and Frank turned to Gladys and said *"Do you still say David will not go on?"*, and she again affirmed her conviction that he would not. Simon and Frank were shown into Birkett's chambers and after a wait of some five minutes he arrived with profound apologies for being delayed. He had scarcely started to pronounce on the likely procedure in Court when an usher announced that Sir Patrick wished to speak to Birkett on the telephone. Birkett withdrew to take the call and returned ten minutes later to report that David was prepared to withdraw his case on the terms that both sides paid their own costs. They were due in Court in half an hour so a quick decision had to be taken. After some hesitation and advice from Birkett it was agreed that Frank should accept as this would avoid washing a lot of dirty linen in public.

Probably David thought Frank would never face the ordeal, but when Frank finally called his bluff he didn't dare risk the case. It's also likely that overnight Birkett had communicated to Hastings that Frank Green would fight and this brought the decisive message on the final day.

David's actions over the next three or four years show clearly that he wished to make a settlement not least because Frank could not live for ever and if some working arrangement between Greens and Seniors could be made he would be able to gain control in the long run. A number of approaches were made which might have succeeded but bringing the law suit had hardened Frank's heart. About this time he wrote to Livsey who had been appointed Managing Director of E Green & Son and to Smallwood who was still the Company Secretary so that they would know his views about the possibility of his coming to terms with the members of the family who had started Seniors and could pass them on to Green's employees who might well be speculating on the future of the Company and their own careers. Frank made it clear that he himself could not be on friendly terms with his relations, with the possible exception of his brother Lycett, who was old and had recently lost his wife. He thought that Green's people might feel reconciliation was in the interest of shareholders and would bring about an immediate increase in profit. Frank, as Chairman, did not think that an association with David, Peter, Armstrong and Heenan could be to the advantage of the

Company and he would resist this to the utmost. However, if Greens were threatened by loss of business with firms like Babcocks who had come to terms with Seniors and was bought out, he Frank would arrange for the heads of department to be compensated.

After the lawsuit dust had settled other suggestions for reconciliation with Seniors rather than bitter competition and cut prices were continuously looked for by David. Towards the end of 1937 McKinstry informed Livsey that David had again been asking him to be more helpful and at least to be less hostile to Seniors. He had suggested that there might be some form of price agreement but McKinstry turned this down as it would give Seniors a share of their market and would result in less work for Greens from Babcock. However, in subsequent discussion with Livsey, McKinstry said he thought the time might be ripe for a meeting between the partners under his Chairmanship to see if something could be done.

Such a meeting took place on December 19th and McKinstry proposed a scheme whereby Greens could control or determine the activities of Seniors. David would not agree to anything on such terms because he would be letting down International Combustion who had been his real friends. In the course of the meeting David mentioned that in their first year (only nine months) they had made a heavy loss and that in 1935 there would also be a loss but current orders would show a profit. Moreover, there was sufficient new business in power stations for Seniors to be bound to obtain a share. David and Peter, who was also present, put forward counter proposals generally on the lines that Wakefield go for the industrial market and Senior the power station market. This was really going back to the old Eco Power situation with Seniors controlling the high pressure business.

At the end of the meeting David was asked to propose the price he would require for Seniors to be bought out and alternatively David asked Livsey to discuss with Frank the purchase of just 48% of Seniors.

Early in the New Year Usher rang Livsey to make an appointment for David to meet. He was not permitted by his shareholders to mention a definite figure for the sale of Seniors but suggested £250,000. As regards keeping both organisations in existence it was obvious that David, having got his freedom, would not once more 'put his head in the lion's mouth' and equally he would not expect Frank to do so.

A month later David was again in touch with Livsey and withdrew any mention of the sale price for 48% of Seniors he had previously made as it was not enough. He then made more suggestions about some sort of quota arrangement. Livsey summed up the conversation in his memo to Frank, saying *"All his proposals are really so absurd that they are not worth considering"*.

Nothing came of the suggested negotiations and McKinstry must have agreed with Livsey that David was asking too much. Although David was still writing to McKinstry in March 1938 to try and arrange a meeting between Greens and Seniors, by this time McKinstry had passed on the approach to Kenneth Hague who had become Sales Manager and later was to become Managing Director and Chairman of Babcocks.

The suggested meeting was turned down by all parties and they got down to work as competitors; there was more business available. Greens were not doing too badly and results had improved considerably since the early thirties and Seniors were getting off the ground.

Mrs Edward Lycett Green with Eddie at Ken Hill. By Sir James Shannon RA (1862-1923)

8
Family and Firm 1933 – 1939

The family row and the business split would have been quite different if Frank had let David have his way with Armstrong as his chief executive. Probably Simon would have gone into Greens anyway, although in quite a different position. As things turned out he was spending a good deal of his Cambridge vacation with Frank at Ashwick. But as all the other members of the family except Basil had stopped visiting Frank, he now only had Gladys and Simon to talk with about what was going on.

Simon went on seeing his grandparents and his father at Ken Hill. He was there for his twenty first birthday in July 1933 and Sir Lycett's best horse, Ken Hill, was running in the Summer Handicap, ridden by 'Tich' Fox, won by a comfortable 1 ½ lengths from a horse ridden by Gordon Richards but was disqualified because he had 'crossed' and caused interference with Gordon Richards' horse.

During the Christmas vacation of 1933/34 Simon's grandmother Ethel spoke to him about the family business . She said she realised that Simon was in an embarrassing situation with the final break from Greens which David had just made and advised him to stay on with Frank as *"the time was bound to come when some form of reconciliation would take place"*. This suggests that David had told his family that he thought Frank would give in.

Soon after this conversation Ethel was taken seriously ill and needed a blood transfusion. As in those days there were no blood banks, a donor from the family was needed and David, Vanda Vivian and Simon had their blood tested by a Harley Street consultant. Vanda's was the wrong group; David's was indecisive so Simon's was selected. The transfusion took place at Ken Hill but very sadly about two weeks later Ethel died. She was buried in Bishopthorpe Church, the spire of which could be seen from the gardens at Ashfield. Simon left immediately after the service making an excuse to get a train back to London.

The family all wondered how Lycett would get on without Ethel. Except for arthritis in her hip she had always seemed in much better health than him and appeared to run the family household. This was confirmed by Bernard Leaff, Sir Lycett's faithful old valet who used to tell how, some mornings when he called him, he would complain of not feeling too well and ask Bernard to summon the doctor who lived in the village about two miles away and enjoyed shooting and golf and was a good and jovial doctor. The doctor would arrive at about 8.45 am in his open Vauxhall , guarded by a rather fierce Aberdeen Terrier on the back seat. Bernard would wait by the door for the signal from Sir Lycett to 'bring in the usual' and soon be back with a bottle of champagne and two glasses. Dr Steadman called his treatment *'The Snettisham Sneezer'*, usually a vintage bottle.

Bernard used to say he made a great mistake when he gave up being Sir Lycett's valet and accepted the promotion to butler. As valet he had been Sir Lycett's personal servant, responsible only to him. Evidently Ethel used to ask Bernard whether Sir Lycett was drinking. It seems he had had a bit of a problem with the bottle in mid life but Bernard was always loyal to his boss and evaded such direct questions. However, when he became butler it was a different story because now Lady Green was his boss and when she insisted on answers to similar questions about Sir Lycett's drinking he found himself with split loyalties and eventually decided to leave.

When Seniors was founded Frank had made his position clear to Simon who was just 23, advising him that if he wished to stay in Greens he would have to be seen to be 100% loyal, not only to him but to all the Directors and staff at Wakefield and this would be difficult if he were to continue to see any of his family who had now sided against him. Frank conceded that Simon could see his father but the fact that Simon accepted this stipulation certainly makes him look weak and it must surely have played on his mind to have been cut off from Ken Hill, all his cousins and his uncles. If he had stood up to Frank and refused what would have happened? He was just coming down from Cambridge.

For his first visit to the Works and Head Office a special dinner party was arranged for the heads of departments in Greens at that time. These included H Livsey – Managing Director, A Smallwood – Company Secretary, H Kenyon – Sales Manager, G Tansley – Chief Engineer, A V

Robinson – Works Manager and F Haigh – Foundry Manager. The dinner was held in a private room in the Majestic Hotel, Harrogate and at the conclusion, Livsey made a short speech welcoming Simon into the business and pledging the support of his colleagues.

As I discovered myself, a public school education and a Cambridge Arts degree were not ideal qualifications, for me or for Simon, to go into an engineering business. So Frank arranged that Simon should meet Harold Howitt, a partner in Peat Marwick, Mitchell & Co who suggested that he should become an accountant but Frank thought that this would take too long and wanted Simon to spend time at Wakefield in a proper capacity to show that there was another generation of the Greens in the business. It was, therefore, decided that he should do a crash business training course in the City where he gained some understanding of company law and commercial procedure as well as book-keeping and accountancy.

In the early autumn of 1934 Simon went to Ken Hill to see his father to tell him that he was engaged to Gladys and would be getting married early in the New Year. His father was flabbergasted. The age difference was ridiculous; he should wait at least six months to come to his senses, etc. Soon after his father must have told his sister Nancy who immediately called on Gladys and was very offensive about the whole idea. But despite his family's feelings Simon and Gladys got married. His family had already been put out of bounds by Frank and Simon didn't see most of them for many years.

Frank's behaviour beggars belief. He had blocked David's career to the point where, utterly frustrated, he broke away and it was only later learned that Simon had been pressured into marrying Gladys as a condition for coming into the firm, with the further condition that he must never speak to or see the rest of his family. It's hardly surprising that Nancy was so rude to Gladys.

Frank insisted that Simon should sell Eaton Farm to raise cash for his marriage settlement. So Simon wrote to his grandfather explaining his predicament, giving him first refusal at the valuation price. So Eaton was bought back into the Ken Hill estate which of course was no bad thing for the shoot!

In his original script Simon writes that *"at the time he somewhat regretted"* that Frank insisted on him making the marriage settlement.

On the eve of his marriage Stephen wrote to Simon giving him brotherly good wishes in spite of everything. He didn't enlarge on the business split but referring to Simon's marriage he wrote *"by your action you have enabled Frank to play the ace"*. This rings true and Simon himself wrote *" if I hadn't been on the scene to take Frank's side (as his heir apparent) he would have had little motive, at his age, to keep on the struggle"*. This clearly suggests that Frank deliberately set up Simon's marriage as a condition for his future role in the firm to strengthen his own position. A pretty dirty trick!

Frank had given Gladys the remaining 25 years of the lease of 186 Ebury Street as part of her wedding present so this became Simon's first home. It was convenient for him to continue his business studies in the City, going to Wakefield for two days about twice a month. In March Simon was made a Director (aged 24) and largely to learn the business, attended many departmental sub-committees which were the basis of monthly directors' reports. From these Frank would often ask questions for Simon to investigate in Wakefield. Most of these committees had been abandoned by David and Armstrong, but when Livsey took over he got them reinstated.

He also spent time with Livsey meeting important customers and suppliers and attending engineering institution dinners to reassure people that Greens would be carrying on with another Green in the business.

Over the next two or three years Simon spent more and more time in Wakefield where Green's fortunes were faring pretty well. The departure of the Senior men had galvanised Greens staff into activity but Livsey had no easy task even after Armstrong left as he had to implement many of the recommendations in the Report of Peat, Marwick, Mitchell & Co for the reduction of overheads. He also had to rebuild the sales side with Kenyon, the Sales Manager who was not an engineer but conscientiously organised his sales team of nine home sales representatives and seven or eight overseas representatives and also agents in other countries, where Greens were not directly represented. France and the USA had subsidiary companies with their own sales organisation and manufacture. (See Appendix A and B.)

9
Engineers and Freemasons

In the days of the vertical tubed economiser it was not really necessary for sales representatives to have had a thorough engineering training though many of them learned enough through experience erecting economisers on site. It was said that to size up a vertical economiser on an existing Lancashire Boiler you only needed an umbrella. First you spat on the flue between the boiler and the chimney and the time that it took for this to evaporate gave you the approximate temperature of the waste gases. Then you counted umbrella lengths for height, width and depth: with this information you could determine the size and performance of the appropriate economiser! On a per tube calculation the representative could give the customer a quick price and a calculation of the fuel saving he could expect. Sometimes an order would be written out by the customer on this information alone.

At this time the greatly expanding electrical power generating field was vital for Greens. The working pressures of the new power station boilers required a stronger design and the Foster economiser sales had been handled by the Eco Power subsidiary under Dundas Heenan who had proved himself a super salesman but had joined Seniors. So Greens had to rebuild connections in this much more technical field. Proposals required close work with the boilermaker to meet specifications and, in most cases, the boilermaker would offer an alternative of either Seniors' or their own design and manufacture, so the customer's mechanical or electrical engineer had to be seen by a Greens representative who could fully understand the technical issues.

George Tansley, Greens Chief Engineer, had joined in 1899 as a young BSc from Manchester University. He was Green's first professionally qualified engineer and Frank had persuaded his father that such an appointment was necessary. Sir Edward, who was a practical engineer never took to this innovation. If there was a technical problem he would say *"Send it to that young man with his brown polished button boots"*. Tansley had laid the foundation of Green's technical procedure and design alterations required to meet the new problems. By about 1925 Green's Engineering Department was further strengthened by employing a young Leeds University BSc, Otto Kubalek whose father had left Czechoslovakia for Leeds. Kubalek was fluent in German and could read any German engineering text book in the field of heat transfer. He spent much of his early days working on heat transfer calculations for cast iron gilled tube economisers which were starting to replace the old vertical design. He was both a mechanical and an electrical engineer and founder member of the Institute of Fuel. He lectured at Institution and Association meetings and got himself known in the industry. So it was decided that both Tansley and Kubalek should go into the power station selling field to counter the activities of Seniors and Heenan. Kubalek also visited Green's representatives overseas including trips of Australia and South American.

Kubalek's Masonic connections helped his sales efforts. He had become a Mason whilst in West Africa and with only a handful of white men in his locality he had advanced pretty rapidly in the Masonic hierarchy. The Masonic ritual appealed to his Teutonic blood and throughout his active life he was an ardent member of the Order.

When Simon joined Greens he had been warned by Livsey that Kubalek might try and influence him to become a Mason. Livsey, having belonged to a Lodge, had seen corruption and dishonesty at first hand and despised the Masonic movement. Unfortunately Simon doesn't seem to have cottoned onto the influential power position that Kubalek was building up for himself and his Masonic cronies within the company. With Cyril Parris and Arthur Tillotson he created a Masonic 'glass ceiling' above which the younger engineers and scientists could not gain promotion unless they 'came on the Square'. This meant that in the post war period when Greens should have been reorganising and building a significant technical team to take the company forward, six or seven up and coming young engineers seeing their future was blocked by the Masonic regime, left the company. Stan Jewson was one of these and decided to emigrate to Canada. He wrote:-

"Any new ideas put forward by the up and coming were always given what was known as the one-two-three. Namely **'It's no bloody**

good', 'It will not work' and 'We tried that thirty years ago'"

When Simon rejoined the company in 1945 after the war, as Chairman, he brought with him a brother officer Francis Copham and another Army officer Charles Larking whom he had met in North Africa. Charles ran the French company until 1957 when he returned to England to become Sales Director; Francis came straight to Wakefield and was appointed Company Secretary. Neither Charles nor Francis had engineering knowledge and in fairness, Simon himself, being non-technical and with no top level engineering advisers other than Kubalek, would have been in a very difficult position if, recognising the malign Masonic influence, he had tried to get rid of Kubalek. In fact from his personal account of events Simon seems to have failed to appreciate what was going on. He writes:

> *"... after the war when (Masonry) was very much in vogue and it was found that nearly all the young engineers in Greens were joining, I was not greatly concerned."*

He was not concerned because he was kept in the dark by Kubalek.

Simon's script reveals that misinformation was being given to him. He writes

> *"Stan Jewson had been one of the most promising young men who had started his career with Greens in the Works and had progressed through the Drawing Office and technical school to the stage where he was on the promotion list. It was not long after he had been assigned to assist Cyril Parris that I was informed he wished to leave as he intended to emigrate to Canada".*

Cyril Parris was of course one of Kubalek's Masonic cronies.

Simon was entirely dependent on Kubalek and his Masonic colleagues for technological advance and it would have been very difficult indeed to loosen their stranglehold without getting rid of them.

My own experience in the three years (1955 – 1958) that I worked for Greens confirms, for me at least, that Simon had no idea why so many excellent young engineers were leaving. Initially I was sent to the French factory and for four months worked as a labourer in the foundries. I was then sent to Paris and went out with Green's fitters to install economisers all over France for eight months. Then, after a short spell in the Design and Costing department in Paris, I was sent to Sulzer Brothers in Wintertur, Switzerland for six months and then returned to work alongside the Works Manager Jimmy Briggs in Wakefield.

In January 1957 an enormous dinner party for all Green's employees was given in Wakefield to celebrate the 21st Birthday of Simon's only child, Rose. With over 1000 employees the dinner had to be held on two successive nights. I sat at the top table and on both nights Simon announced in his speech that it was excellent '*to have young Adrian, a member of the family, coming in and doing so well'*. There were embarrassingly loud cheers.

About ten months later, with one of Kubalek's young engineers, I drove across the Pennines to Ruabon, a village in North Wales where Monsanto had recently commissioned a Greens economiser. We were to check its performance by measuring the chimney draft and photographing its cleaning procedure, in action. This was a messy job and before getting into our car for the long drive home we asked for some rags and white spirit to clean ourselves up a bit. We left feeling a good job had been well done. The following morning I was summoned to see Simon who told me that Kubalek had been telephoned from the Monsanto plant and told that we were in dead trouble because we had filled the local river with the polluted effluent from the cleaning procedure. We were also told that we had been 'unacceptably rude'. Simon told me to leave for Cambridge immediately and the young engineer got severely reprimanded.

Twenty years later Simon himself told me this had been a carefully planned Masonic set-up. The conduit piping to take the effluent away safely had been removed before we arrived and we were then falsely accused of polluting the local river. The conduit was anyway not part of the Green's installation.

Kubalek had his own plans for management succession at Greens and they didn't include young engineers who refused to become Masons or were members of the family!

We were clearly the victims of a very unpleasant regime and were probably lucky to escape. But the incident does point up the impossibility of Simon's position as a non-technical, untrained manager in what should have been on the way to becoming a serious high technology company – which is in fact what Senior Engineering were able to do.

It was always on the cards that Kubalek would be promoted and would succeed Tansley as Chief Engineer and Livsey feared that he would be after his job as MD before long. Whilst holding him back Livsey assured Kubalek that he would get promotion but also advised him that if he wanted to be a senior executive in a British firm he should change his name to something sounding a bit more British. This hurt his feelings, despite which he changed his name to John Rylands.

In the early years of competition with Seniors one of Green's problems was that Heenan, as the ex-salesman of the Foster Economiser, was well aware of some of its technical weaknesses and knew of installations which were giving trouble. Some of the first Fosters had been banked too high and too close together and were very difficult to clean. Heenan exploited these difficulties, claiming that the new Senior Economiser 'H' tube design was much more practical and could be more easily cleaned although customers quickly pointed out that this was only partially true. So Greens decided that some alteration to the shape of the tubes was needed. A test plant at Wakefield tried out every conceivable form and size of tube with different shapes and pitches of gills to measure and compare heat transfer efficiency with reasonable access for cleaning. The Senior design was also tested to compare its efficiency with Greens new design. Eventually the Premier Diamond Economiser with its diamond bodied tube and rectangular gill and with the tubes arranged in staggered formation providing diagonal passages for rodding from the sides, was launched. But in Stan Jewson's direct experience it was an uphill struggle competing against the 'H' tube.

As a qualified mechanical engineer Livsey was particularly interested in manufacturing problems. There had been little or no improvement of plant for several years. So Livsey encouraged the purchase of new equipment to machine the new cast iron gilled tubes on a production line.

During Livsey's years of office from when he took over until the war, there was a steady improvement. But perhaps he was fortunate that he hit a period when trade was improving. Results would have been better if it had not been for the Senior competition. But if it had not been Seniors' it would have come from some other company. For example, George Usher was supporting the rise of the Superheater Co which was threatening to enter the high pressure market. If David and Seniors had not gone along with his plans Usher might well have encouraged Superheater to compete against Greens.

Foster Marine economiser

10
The 1939 – 1945 War

In the Autumn of 1936 Livsey suggested that Simon should visit Greens' American subsidiary as no one had been to see them for ten years. There he found a moribund management and recommended that Livsey go over himself to sort things out. He was also given another assignment which was the beginning of an important development for Greens in the marine market. The Foster Wheeler Corporation in the USA was installing its Foster design in ships with an improved aluminium protected steel tube for use in naval vessels. Under the terms of the purchase of the Foster Economiser patents Greens were entitled to any improvements and Simon obtained further detailed new design drawings and samples. Greens immediately started to try and sell these designs in the UK but with little success as marine engineers were super conservative.

However, shortly before the war Foster Wheeler had become more active with an English subsidiary, Foster Wheeler Ltd, and persuaded Livsey that Greens would always find it difficult to sell marine economisers on their own and that Foster Wheeler intended to become active in the British Marine field by licensing shipbuilders to fabricate their design of boiler. They wanted to specify Foster economisers which were an integral part of their boilers but needed Greens specialised technique for manufacture and proposed an agreement whereby, in the marine market, Foster Wheeler would design and sell and Greens manufacture. During the war and for many years thereafter this became a major source of business for Greens.

In 1937 Frank decided to give up hunting and leave Ashwick. During the season, aged 75, Frank still hunted on over a hundred days so it was a surprise when he suddenly gave it up but his excuse was that he wanted to see more of Simon's daughter in London.

Whilst Frank was at Ashwick Simon used to go down frequently for the weekend to hunt and shoot and when Ashwick was closed Frank paid for his horses with his stud groom and stablemen to stay at the George Hotel, Grantham so that after Christmas of 1937 Simon could still go on hunting.

The war clouds were building up over Czechoslovakia and that summer air-raid shelters at the back of houses in London were being constructed and there were not many who really believed that peace would last. Greens were approached by the Ministry of Supply about making munitions as they had in the First World War. Livsey had just constructed a large new shop for flash welding bends onto high pressure economiser tubes so this new shop and its extension was turned into a production line for the manufacture of 3.5 ins anti-aircraft shells.

By this time Simon was acting as deputy to Livsey and therefore became involved in all that was going on, but in August he was called up and Greens forgot about economiser competition and concentrated on the war effort.

The economiser business still went on as factories still needed steam to generate power to keep them going and as many of them were working day and night more repairs and replacements than usual were required. Also the demand for power stations still existed and new Royal Ordnance Factories were being built all over the country, many of them in more remote areas away from enemy bombing. The Wakefield area was particularly fortunate in avoiding any serious raids.

Greens had just started on the production of anti-aircraft shells when the war started and female labour was recruited to take the place of men who were called up. About half way through the war production was switched to making 4.5 ins shells, so with land available on the East side of the Works it was agreed to build a new shop for shell production with two production lines - the finished shells waiting in the middle to go into a Ministry of Supply inspection area before despatch to the explosives-filling factories.

When the old shell shop was vacated it was required for marine work which was in line with the traditional business. Under the arrangement with Foster Wheeler Ltd virtually no progress in selling had been made and no impression at all had been made on the Navy. However, the pursuit of the German battle cruiser 'Graf Spee' to the South Atlantic and her shelling in the mouth of the River Plate turned things round.

British destroyers had been forced to drop out of the chase but some

American destroyers managed to keep going and were able to keep the *Graf Spee* in view and eventually sank her. Not surprisingly, Winston Churchill was soon asking why the British destroyers had run out of fuel and the American vessels had had a greater steaming range. The answer was that the Americans were equipped with Foster Wheeler boilers and economisers. The Navy duly took note and in consequence all capital ships from destroyers upwards were to be equipped with Greens' Foster Wheeler economisers. Livsey went to London to arrange details with Foster Wheeler and to Bath to see the Royal Navy engineers. Much preparatory work had to be done and fifteen-ton cranes erected for these economisers to be assembled in Wakefield in blocks and transported to the shipyards,lifted into ships and coupled up to their boilers.

The advantage of Greens' Foster Wheeler economisers for marine use with the efficient Foster Wheeler marine boiler was also quickly noted by the designers and builders of British merchant marine vessels and so Greens supply of these began to increase rapidly.

This work was well under way when Simon returned to the UK in the spring of 1943, wounded with shrapnel in his foot and he was on sick leave for most of the summer. But he managed a trip to Wakefield to see how things were going. Whilst he was there Livsey implored him to try and get his release from the Army as he was feeling the strain. If the war had not come he would have retired in 1940.

Shortly afterwards Livsey asked Simon to go to Wakefield to meet the Head Admiralty Engineering Officer in the district. Livsey had told him that he feared his health would not allow him to carry on as Managing Director and that before the war Simon had been training as his understudy to take his place. The Admiral asked Simon if he would come out of the Army and Simon explained that his release was not possible. A short time later he was sent for by his Commanding Officer in Hereford and informed that he was to be given temporarily release, immediately.

Simon had a great deal to catch up with at Wakefield and Livsey gave him the greatest possible help. There had not been many changes in the senior management as most of them were too old for military service. Rylands had taken over as Chief Engineer and his department was still mostly concerned with technical calculations for the extended surface economisers. Standardisation had never been achieved as it had been for the vertical economiser and each tender had to have its own drawings showing the layout of the boiler plant and the economiser. The economiser itself was an assembly of standard parts, but most contracts also included special casings and ducting. Often fans had to be incorporated which were bought from outside suppliers. Production of 4.5 inch shells was still not able to work to capacity due to materials supply delays. The Works Manager Robinson's priority was to speed up production as 'D' Day was approaching and maximum output was required to stock up for the invasion by working around the clock. Efforts were hampered by the delays in delivering copper and steel but when these problems were explained to the visiting Minister of Supply, Sir Andrew Duncan, he gave little encouragement and insisted on a 25% step up of production, which all concerned knew was impossible.

All the war contracts were costed which kept the accountancy staff busy keeping records and negotiating with government departments. The shell contract was straightforward as the material was 'free supply', with wages and agreed overheads paid plus a small profit. Economiser contracts for government plants were not so straightforward. Sub-contractors to boilermakers could be at a disadvantage for their ordinary commercial business if their prices were driven down by the main contractors. It was therefore agreed that Greens should quote a normal competitive price and afterwards, if the Government department found any excess profit, they would be repaid.

However, Admiralty contracts involving Foster Wheeler economisers had rather different complications because Foster Wheeler did not want Greens to deal directly with the Admiralty and sought a Court injunction to prevent direct dealing. The Admiralty successfully defeated this and encouraged by being able to operate separately from Foster Wheeler on Admiralty contracts, Livsey also started to deal direct with Canadian Pacific line who were building Beaver class merchant vessels. The boilers for these had previously been designed by one of their own engineers and Greens adapted a small standard Premier Diamond economiser to be supplied with them. A clause in the Foster Wheeler agreement gave Greens the right to supply other boilermakers but thought that the introduction of a different tube design was not within the spirit of the Agreement and a protracted legal argument ensued and was only finally sorted out after the war had ended.

11

Post War Greens: Stan Jewson takes on the Masons

When the war in Europe was over business rapidly changed back to peace time requirements. By now Livsey had gone to Bournemouth and only paid occasional visits to Wakefield. He died very soon of cancer.

The formation of The Central Electricity Generating Board had a dramatic effect on the design of generators and boilers. 60 MW units were the order of the day in the immediate post war period but during the next ten years the size of units grew almost annually so that in the sixties 500 MW units became the standard.

This meant fewer larger boilers were required and likewise fewer larger economisers. The effect of this was to increase the competition with Seniors since there were fewer orders to go round. The cast iron sleeve designs were considered unsuitable for modern boiler designs. Flue gas and water temperatures being much higher there was no need for cast iron protection and all-steel designs were called for.

Greens offered a plain steel tube design and several were installed. The problem was that these units were really no different to superheaters

Stan Jewson with Archie Johnson

the construction of which was always considered to be an integral part of the boiler. The question arose, why should the boilermakers give away part of their order for something which could be readily made in their own workshops?

Seniors came up with a different solution. They welded fins onto the steel tubes to extend the heating surface and thereby reduce the size and cost of the economiser. Greens had no alternative but to follow suit as quickly as possible. A machine was purchased from Sweden which could weld pairs of fins onto the steel tube. There was little to choose between the two designs and decisions on contracts usually boiled down to who had the lowest price.

It should be noted that Welded Steel Gill (WSG) economisers did not have staggered tube formation but were in-line and with the pairs of fins attached and looked remarkably similar to the old Seniors cast iron 'H tube design' sleeve.

Competition became fierce and Seniors seemed to have an edge on price. The reason for this was that their economiser had tubes at five inch pitch horizontal and vertical whereas Greens had tubes at four inch pitch. This meant that for a given heating surface Greens needed to supply more tubes and more tube welds, both of which were expensive. Stan Jewson was personally involved in trying to get the Green design changed to five inch pitch in order to better compete but Engineering Department (namely Mr. Parris) would not budge. The largest Power Station in Britain (Drax) was coming up for bids and there was several years of work at stake. Finally Simon Green called a meeting of all interested parties to thrash the matter out. The decision was made to change the design to five inch pitch. The Drax contract was won along with several more contracts overseas and at last it seemed that Greens had the edge on Seniors.

Rapid expansion of power generation was taking place in South Africa. Unfortunately because of restrictions on currency exchange it was becoming increasingly difficult to export equipment from Wakefield. Accordingly in 1970 a new factory and manufacturing facility was built in Vereeniging some thirty miles from Joannesburg, which came on line just in time to take advantage of Greens new competitive edge on Seniors and the South African company made a clean sweep of the available contracts.

It was about this time that Simon Green received a letter from Cyril Parris accusing Stan Jewson of abusing him and telling him that he was only fit for the scrap heap. He had a witness to this 'altercation'. Simon gave Stan the letter to read and he was totally amazed having never ever said a 'wrong' word. He demanded that Parris be confronted forthwith together with his witness. Stan writes *'Simon Green just chuckled and told me to forget about it since he didn't believe a word of it. Doubtless he found the letter reminiscent of a telephone call some years earlier about Adrian Bridgewater. Freemasonry was once again rearing its head and history was repeating itself although unsuccessfully on this occasion'.*

The industrial applications for economisers had diminished very considerably because of the new, efficient package boilers which did not need economisers. Also the marine market for Foster economisers which had been so lucrative for many years was disappearing because of the change from steam ships to diesel. The cast iron air heater on which so much time and effort had been spent was a failure. One order was obtained for Bankside Power Station but it was not considered to be a success. It was apparent that if Greens were to continue to grow they must diversify.

The diesel ships which had suddenly become all the fashion no longer needed boilers for propulsion but auxiliary boilers were installed for other services. In the case of oil tankers a substantial amount of steam was used to heat the cargo of crude oil in order to reduce its viscosity to make it more easily pumped ashore. Time was money to a shipowner and speeding up pumping meant a quicker turn around, It was noted by Greens young engineers that the diesel engines exhaust gases were of a temperature which was capable of generating steam for cargo heating without burning valuable fuel. Using the WSG heating surface a steam generator was designed and the "Diesecon" was born. Messrs _Parris and Tillotson were both very much against the idea and considered it a complete waste of time but in the event it was a great success and units were exported to wherever ships were being built. Like the Foster economisers the Diesecons were works assembled and shipped as one piece.

As mentioned above Archibald Johnston supplied replacement elements for Howden Ljungstrom air heaters. The business was largely confined to special elements for small power stations which Howdens were not too concerned about. There was no production line and production was inefficient. The CEGB selected the type of element best suited to the fuel being used in the boilers. Some elements fouled up more quickly than others and the selection was made accordingly. By this time the production of the replacement elements had been transferred to Wakefield together with most of the production staff. It came to Stan's notice that the CEGB wished to install a type of element known as the Double Undulated but were frustrated because Howdens said it could not be made at a competitive price. Stan devised a method of manufacturing the element and with the help of the Tool Room produced several samples which he proudly carried to London to show to the CEGB. Furthermore he indicated that if they were to order a complete replacement for a 500MW unit Greens would supply it at the same price as the standard elements. The CEGB agreed and on the strength of that one contract Greens installed a modern production line which could produce every kind of element. The line was kept running 24 hours a day seven days a week from the day the installation was complete. Stan writes *"My only regret is that it was installed immediately outside my office and the noise it made was unbelievable. The only redeeming feature was a particularly noisy press in the line which operated at 120 strokes per minute, I calculated earned sixpence at every stroke"*.

It was clear that Power Station orders would reduce as the installed generating capacity was now capable of meeting foreseeable needs. Greens needed another tubular heat exchanger which could mitigate against the drop in economiser requirements. The solution to this problem came not from conserving energy but by dissipating it. Oil Refineries were being built not only in this country but all over the world. Many of the plant designs for the oil refineries were carried out in this country and they utilised many heat exchangers for cooling the product between the various stages of refining. The heat exchangers involved consisted of one inch diameter steel tubes on which an aluminum fin was helically wound. The pitch of the fins was very close sometimes as close as ten fins per inch. Some of the units operated at very high pressure requiring high grade welding skills for the manifolds. Such skills Greens had in plenty. After some research it was discovered that the specialised machines for winding the fins could only be purchased in the USA and several were bought and were installed in Wakefield and two more in the newly expanded factory in S.A. In a very short period Green became a major supplier of 'Heating Coils'.

The demand for steel tubes to satisfy the requirements for economisers and heating coils grew very quickly and it soon became apparent that there was insufficient capacity worldwide and our ability to meet delivery dates was being adversely affected. It seemed the best solution was to manufacture our own steel tubes. The techniques employed in tube manufacture were already familiar so it was not a difficult step but considerable capital expenditure was required to purchase the tube mill and a large factory building to house it. The tube mill was a success and contracts to absorb any surplus capacity were easily obtained. However this diversification step did not go unnoticed by Senior Engineering. They had a large subsidiary company Phoenix Steel Tube who took a dim view of Greens entering the market. Stan had already had contact with the M.D. of Seniors about cast iron air heater tubes which they desperately needed and were unable to source and which he had agreed to supply from Greens foundry. During a visit about the air heater tubes the MD of Phoenix came and pleaded with Greens not to enter the steel tube market and offered to supply all requirements. Needless to say the offer was declined but contact was established with Seniors and meetings were held at infrequent intervals to discuss common interests. This was an important step as later events were to prove.

When Stan Jewson was offered the Group Managing Director job it was on the basis of a five year rolling service agreement with a minimum of three years' service to run if either party wished to terminate. However there was also an agreement that if he were to continue in the job until he was fifty five he would be free to retire if he wished, on full pension. That would mean doing the MD job for ten years. In the event he held the job for eleven years and having given the job everything he had got, he informed Simon that he was ready to hand over the reins. Stan had always maintained that that if a chief executive could not fulfil his plans in ten years he should not have had the job in the first place. The job was given to Alf Tyson, a Greens man who had been appointed to run the chemical company when it was acquired. This he had done very successfully. Simon asked Stan to stay on as Deputy Chairman. His whole working life had been in a very much hands on role and having done the Managing Directors job for eleven years he felt it was inevitable that sooner or later he would be bound to interfere with the new MD. Nevertheless he continued in this role until Simon clarified his plan for the future. His plan was for Stan to become Chairman and in order to maintain the family connection he (Simon) would assume a nominal role as President. Stan didn't need to think about Simon`s plan and immediately said *"Count me out I have no wish to become Chairman"*. Simon`s immediate reply was *"Well if you are going so am I. I have no wish to start again with someone else"*. And there the matter rested.

It was some little time later that Stan had lunch with Geoff Deverson, Group MD of Seniors. Geoff rather jokingly suggested that the two companies ought to consider getting together. Stan made no reply but reported the conversation back to Simon who in turn brought it up at the next Board Meeting. Stan was surprised by the reception this received.

John Sheffield who was by far the most influential Non Executive Director, immediately said the suggestion should be given serious consideration. Sheffield was expecting vociferous objections from Stan and was surprised when Stan wholeheartedly agreed with him. Sheffield, who was Chairman of several companies, did not make his comments lightly. He said that he foresaw difficult times ahead for capital plant manufacturers especially in the power generation and petro-chemical industries and Stan immediately agreed with him. Whereas currently Greens was very profitable with full order books, five years down the road things could look very different. It was agreed that Deverson and Stan should meet again with Simon present to explore the possibilities. The rest is history.

What later happened is interesting. Not a single new power station, either oil or coal fired has been ordered to this day since the Drax order. The dash for gas encouraged the installation of dozens of gas turbine plants within existing power stations to increase generating capacity but not a single steam turbine or steam generator has been ordered. It it's a similar story in the Petro Chemical Industry, not a single new refinery has been built in Britain. In fact there have been several closures.

After the takeover Seniors moved all economiser manufacturing to Wakefield. Surprisingly they also took over Foster Wheeler who were obviously feeling the pinch from the lack of marine orders. The company then became known as Senior Foster Wheeler. Seniors cannot have found the heat exchanger market a bed of roses. They eventually sold out to an American company Thermal Engineering International (TEI). By this time the number of employees had fallen from well over a thousand to just fifty four. Sadly even at this level TEI continued to struggle and finally went into administration in 2005 marking the end of economiser manufacture in Wakefield.

June 1963. Visit to the Greens of the Yorkshire Divisional council,
National Society for Clean Air. Seated front row left to right:
Cyril Parris, John Rylands and Arthur Tillotson (the masonic block)
Centre: Simon Green and behind him the dark haired Stan Jewson.

12
The Wasted Opportunity

In an Annex to Simon's original script dealing with Green's Italian subsidiary (Appendix B 4) one can see how Green's engineering department refused to accept his ideas. Dealing with the misdemeanours of one Feruccio Casinghini the Italian firm's Director, who consistently failed to pay licence fees within agreed time limits and with whom trading relationships were terminated, Simon wrote:

> *"Casinghini was a thoughtful and progressive thinker and Wakefield might well have developed more of his ideas if it had not been for a reluctance by the (Greens) engineering staff to accept the ideas of our little Italian friend".*

This attitude, encapsulated by Stan Jewson as *'Not invented here',* frustrated the young engineers in Wakefield who couldn't stand the domination of an inner cabal of Masonic engineers from an earlier generation, so they left the Company.

Innovation, beyond modifications to the economiser, simply did not happen.

Diversification into logically related products did not happen.

In any company there is the exciting start-up stage when a new invention is first promoted and a number of related products, based on the new technology, come into the market. Contemporary examples include Dyson with their vacuum cleaners, fans and hand-dryers. In the '50s' Jeremy Fry's valve actuators were the foundation rock of Rotork. These and may other inventors quickly surround themselves with teams of top flight engineers and scientists and create a 'pipeline' of innovation.

Apple Computers are said to have enough new products in their pipeline to ensure growth over the next decade.

Old Edward Green and his son Sir Edward were both entrepreneurs and inventors but three generations on John Rylands was chief engineer but had no innovation pipeline. He seems to have deliberately created an innovation blockage in Wakefield and stamped on any idea 'not invented here', but invented nothing himself. Simon hints at this problem when writing about Casinghini but fails to recognise an important aspect of it when he writes about young engineers refusing to become freemasons and leaving the firm.

Unlike Old Neddy and his son Edward, Frank and Simon seem merely to have presided over the exploitation of an out-dated technology though facing competition from imitators.

David found Frank impossible to work with, dictating administrative rules from Somerset, and unwilling to invest in anything new. So David first tried to innovate away from Wakefield with Con Econ in a London office but Frank saw this as 'a sinister plot' and blocked David's plans, forcing him to take off and launch Senior Economisers.

Simon was in on all of Frank's policies and strategies but appears to have learnt nothing from the Senior's break-away. Was he blocked and frustrated by Rylands' Masons or couldn't he see the fundamental innovation weakness?

Only when Stan Jewson came back from America to become Managing Director did new concepts and radical engineering solutions start to appear, perhaps for the first time since old Neddy and Sir Edward's days.

Several major decisions still caused serious tensions between the old Masonic cabal of outdated engineers and Jewson, who was even reported to Simon by Cyril Parris for allegedly telling him that he was 'fit for the scrapheap'. Simon ignored this. And for his last ten years with Greens Economiser Group Stan Jewson was able to refocus the company's technological capability enabling it to compete profitably and to be sold at a very realistic price to Seniors.

Senior Engineering is now a leading player in the aeronautical engineering industry with Boeing and Airbus amongst its customers. Would a merged company led by David have wasted fewer opportunities to innovate and exploit the originally powerful Greens brand?

APPENDIX A

GREENS UK SUBSIDIARIES

1 J W Harrision Limited

Harrison's main business connection was with collieries but they were suppliers of castings for Greens over a period of years. After the 1914-18 war the demand from Greens became so great that old Mr Harrison approached Greens with an offer to sell his firm which was accepted and their total output went to Greens who extended the factory.

All went well until the general slump in the second half of the 1920s. The demand from Greens dropped off and Harrisons were left on their own to look for outside work which was not easy and any business obtained was at low prices.

By the time Simon arrived at Greens Harrisons were still making the scrapers with their bars and guards, required for the vertical economisers and for these parts there was a large repair and replacement demand. They were also getting sales from outside customers, in particular from Joseph Rhodes & Sons Ltd, an old established Wakefield engineering firm specialising in presses and shears for steel plate.

A more realistic price for castings supplied to Greens by Harrisons was agreed and the Company was able to stand on its own feet.

After the war demand grew once more and Greens were calling on Harrisons for more and more castings, with a wider range of types. John Rylands joined the Board and, with Webster, evolved various methods of increasing production and for several years the Company was extremely busy. But as the post war boom was coming to an end engineering generally was faced with a trend towards more and more welded steel fabrications in place of iron casting and Greens was on exception with a drop in turnover for both Harrisons and Greens foundries. It was decided to close down Harrisons and transfer its workforce to Greens.

This was a logical decision which proved, over the years, to be a wise one as it became necessary for Greens to have an outside connection when the demand for economiser castings reduced to a level when it would have been barely viable for them for this purpose along. In making the decision to move Harrisons production a factor had been the location of their busy foundry near the centre of Wakefield. Pollution was beginning to attract the attention of the local authorities and to prevent this, large costs would have been necessary in order to remain on the site.

By 1929 it had become obvious to Greens customers that J W

Harrison & Sons Ltd really meant Greens so sales to outside customers were made under the name of E Green & Son (Castings) Ltd. When we moved Harrisons into Greens foundry the division of production tonnage was approximately 75% Greens work and 25% outside. By 1950 these figures had swung right round to 35% Greens and 65% outside.

2   John Kilner & Sons (1927) Ltd

John Kilner & Sons started their Glass Works next door to Greens, on Calder Vale Road in 1865, about the same time as Greens built their Works. A company of that name was formed in 1909 with John William Kilner and Barron Kilner as Chairman and Managing Director.

Kilners prospered during the 1914-18 War and the boom immediately after. Greens were at that time desperate to expand their foundry and had paid a high price for a trip of land on which to build an extension. However, twenty years later pumped concrete and buttresses were needed to prevent its collapse.

In the middle twenties Barron Kilner died and at the same time competition in the glass industry was growing with the new automatic machining and the company got into financial difficulties and a liquidator was appointed.

Greens had no experience in this field and anxiety was caused by the pile up of stocks mainly for the beer and mineral water bottle trade and bad debts were not infrequent.

During the late nineteen twenties efforts were made with considerable success to replace the brewery business by the manufacture of carboys, demi-johns and glassware for the Chemical trade and blue and amber bottles for pharmaceuticals. This stood the firm in good stead as carboys and larger bottles were required by the Ministry of Supply. The famous Kilner jar used largely for fruit bottling also made good sales.

Visitors who had time to go round the Works were always interested in the glass and particularly the hand blowing of large carboys.

The success of the business depended on the long experience of long-serving managers who were impossible to replace. With these management problems, along with increasing competition from United Glass Bottles, the company became loss making and Simon and Francis Copham, who were the directors of Kilners, got assistance and advice from a friend in the glass trade. He advised that either a large sum should be spent on the installation of mechanised plant, or the company should be closed down. The latter course was taken as the business had only been acquired for the land and expansion and modernisation of the economiser Works was the first priority.

APPENDIX B

GREENS OVERSEAS SUBSIDIARIES AND AGENCIES

Greens had a number of overseas subsidiary companies at various times in France, Germany, Italy, USA, South Africa and Canada as well as trading agencies in other countries including Belgium, India and Australia which were formed from time to time to meet local trading conditions. Local companies were acquired for various reasons. All of them absorbed a good deal of Wakefield Management time and some were not given enough of it. In 1955 when I joined the Company the only Associated Companies were in France and USA with Branch Offices in Belgium, South Africa, India, Australia, Mexico and Canada.

1 Green Fuel Economiser Company Inc - USA

Shortly before the First World War monthly remittances were having to be sent to the Company (GFE) to cover wages and it was discovered that the Sales Manager whose substantial commission was based on turnover, was taking orders at any price. He was dismissed and George Usher was sent out from Greens' German subsidiary in his place.

As time proved, it had been a big mistake not to take Usher's advice and to lose the services of Hagen the top rated fan designer, just when GFE was going into the fan market and the Sturtevent Engineering Company, who were already making fans started to compete against Greens with their own economisers.

C F Nield, who was a partner in Davies and Nield, GFE's auditors, was Greens' chief adviser at this time and also President of GFE. Nield was over cautious and was frightened of User. Usher would not operate under Nield and left, probably as much because of this as the rejection of his proposal to take on Hagen.

During the years when Usher was in charge, the economiser side of the business prospered and with the post war boom, considerable profits were accumulated and invested in short dated Municipal Loans and Guaranteed Mortgages.

But by 1928 the company was not showing a profit and by 1931 the American slump was at its worst and Greens were speculating about whether the company should be closed down with orders and counter orders from David and Peter on the one hand and Frank, the Chairman, on the other.

This was not altogether surprising as the family row was reaching its climax.

It was finally agreed to strip GFE of its reserves and leave the company to earn its own living. Having received about a quarter of a million in sterling, Wakefield was apparently satisfied but GFE was left in a pretty precarious state although they were able to carry on without further injection of capital.

Simon did not visit the Company again until 1948.

By their purchase of the Foster economiser patents in 1927 Greens were excluded from competing in the USA and Canada with extended surface economisers so traditional business was confined to a rapidly declining turnover in Vertical economiser replacements. The company was therefore organised round the sale, manufacture and supply of Mechanical Draught Fans with 5% to 8% of the market, but was faced with rapid technical changes involving higher duty fans needed to meet the demands of larger steam generating boilers.

Main competitors were Sturtevant (who were taken over by Westinghouse), American Blowers, Buffalo Forge and Clarage Fan. The first two were by far the largest and were spending a lot of money on research and claiming higher operating efficiencies. Burkenstock was a member of the American Fan Association which consisted of all the suppliers. Under USA law a price controlling ring was forbidden but it was supposed to exchange technical information. Most of these firms were visited often to see if there was any opportunity to sell them GFE as it seemed difficult to run a small company against much larger competitors. There was also the problem of finding the right man to run the company, particularly as Wakefield had no fan experience.

Attempts were made to revive the sale of cast iron gilled tube economisers and Tillotson went over for about three months. He was able to obtain about half a dozen orders but after his return the selling effort couldn't be sustained. By the time agents, main contractors and other middle men had had their rake off prices rose about 150% above the ex-Works Wakefield price. And also the package boiler was emerging, fired by cheap oil or natural gas which meant that the sale of an economiser was difficult to justify.

In 1954 GFE introduced another line, obtaining a licence to supply Aerodyne Dust Collectors taking on Gert Eiserman and Barney Turenne. As a possible successor, Turenne engaged Ken Gear as Chief Engineer who almost immediately became most insistent that something be done to improve the performance efficiency of the firm's main fan products.

At the same time there was an approach from Archibald Johnstone, in

England. He had been the Yorkshire representative for James Howden & Co after the war and had fallen out with them and had set up on his own supplying replacement elements for regenerative airheaters. Greens had helped him by supplying manufacturing equipment and had also made a small investment in his firm. H ehad good connections with the power station engineers in Yorkshire and the North Midlands and was assisting Greens' sales of cast iron airheaters to the industry.

Meanwhile Greens were informed that Chief Fan Engineer for Howdens, Johann Johnson, had left and set up with two of his colleagues. They needed financial backing and manufacturing. Howdens were the leading suppliers in the UK and this looked a good opportunity for Greens in the USA to improve itself. Unfortunately it emerged that the company was not operating profitably and the GFE manager was not capable of doing his job and had lost the confidence of his executives. Simon dismissed him and immediately appointed a successor with the help of Charles Larking. There was no time to look around outside and they had to look at those who were in the firm.

After final consultation with Allen and Bob Davies they decided to appoint Barney Turenne as temporary Chief Executive and with a new team the company had a short run of success, during which they built up good connections with manufacturers' agents throughout the industrial States. But they were carried away by their initial success and overbuilt their staff and overheads which presented more problems when the trade cycle declined.

During this period another development brought new export work to Wakefield. GFE obtained an enquiry for very low recuperative heat recovery for which cast-iron gilled tubes were appropriate. Initially Greens representative in Canada went to assist with sales and project work but it was soon obvious that to deal with an increase in enquiries a full time representative would be needed.

It was therefore suggested that Stan Jewson who had started his career with Greens and was about to emigrate to Canada might consider representing them there. He accepted but an almighty slump had hit Canada and Toronto seemed to be a dead loss. However, the American low-level economiser project had started to take off and Stan was sent to GFE in Beacon. Over the next few years he took complete charge of several large contracts from sale to site service and was able to prove his personal and technical skills to Wakefield which led to his later appointment to Greens main Board.

Wakefield were beginning to see trouble ahead for GFE and because of a fall off in fan work had started to look for manufacturing work in other fields and thus became involved with government contracts for specialised work which was quite out of keeping with its business. The resultant Grenco Services Company which was set up, proved a disaster.

In 1957 Greens in England had become a public company and when assessing the placing price it was clear that the losses of GFE in the two previous years would pull down the price by about 10p a share and as there was no prospect of immediate recovery it was decided to leave GFE out of the flotation. GFE would have to look to the Green family for future finance which they badly needed. The introduction of Johnnie Johnson designs had never developed and this man created serious problems at Wakefield. But GFE had great hopes for future fan development through their young engineer Gerry Durning who was confident about the future but because the size of fans for the Power Industry was increasing new expensive plant would be required at Beacon. But because Simon was reluctant to finance it privately it was necessary to try and find a buyer for the company as a going concern. The company passed through several hands but when Simon visited them in 1977 Gerry Durning was still there and had had the opportunity to prove his ability as a fan man. The company had become the largest supplier of fans to Public Utilities and the steel industry still on the same site at Beacon but with much larger and better facilities.

So within the space of fifty years Greens had failed to recognise and exploit the skills of two men who reached the summit in fan engineering.

2   S A l'Economiseur Green

Shortly after the first world war Greens found itself facing strong competition in France and needed to gain local manufacturing experience in order to exploit the business which had flourished since the days of Samuel Green. So when M. Lemoine, who had been doing some manufacturing for Greens, approached Samuel Green's son Basil to discuss disposing of his foundry and machine shop Basil arranged for Arthur Smallwood and Gilbert Tennant to go over to negotiate.

"After a short tour of the works and gardens we returned to find the bureau d'etude converted into a salle a manger. This was the side of life that appealed to M. Lemoine. His hard face relaxed, his eyes sparkled as he received his guests in true French fashion – the aperitifs, the white wine, the red wine on the hearth to be served at just the right temperature, the champagne, the liqueurs, a table set out to perfection. There could be no question of considering business in such an

atmosphere. This was the prelude to put everyone in the right frame of mind for the discussion to follow"

Arthur Smallwood
Company Secretary E Green & Son 1919

Following this convivial, extended lunch the French business of Monsieur Julien Lemoine, a member of the Chamber of Deputies, of Hallines, was taken over by Greens. Previously there had been a 'Gentleman's Agreement' between M Lemoine and Edward Green and Son whereby he was able to make a few economisers in his small works at Hallines but was content to pass most orders to Greens and draw commission.

From the early 1920s Basil Green was in charge, living in Paris. The head office was at 32 Rue de Londres. Basil made several visits to England each year spending most of his holidays hunting with Frank on Exmoor. He was assisted by Charles Lipscomb who had joined Greens as a boy.

The Works of the Company were at Blanc Misseron on the Belgian frontier between Valenciennes and Mons and had commenced manufacture there shortly after the end of the first world war as the demand for new plant and repairs from war damage were enormous. Frank and Simon thought that David and Armstrong wanted to keep the manufacture at Wakefield and refused to have anything to do with this subsidiary, insisting that full responsibility for its actions should fall on Basil Green. Consequently they received very little assistance from Wakefield and it was left to Mr Smallwood to pay half yearly visits to prepare cost and management accounts.

It's highly likely that David Green had an ulterior motive in refusing to take any responsibility for the French company because he would have known that Basil was on Frank Green's side. When the breakaway came and Senior Economisers commenced they had acquired the license for the H-tube design from the French competitors, Comeconomiseur, so they had obviously been keeping their eye on the continental market. Also without the knowledge of Basil they had persuaded the chief salesman of SAEG, Mr Scurr to join them.

Basil had with him in Paris as Chief Technical Engineer, Mr Hammond, assisted by a young engineer, Harry Gardiner. The Works was run by Mr Akers who had been a foreman at Wakefield assisted by Mr A Hague who had been in the Wakefield drawing office. In the 1930s they had a difficult time with severe competition from Pont a Mousson and from Comeconomiseur who were spurred on by help from Seniors with new high pressure designs. However the company was making both ends meet and as the investment in it had been repaid no one worried unduly.

As the 1939 war began to loom up Simon asked Basil whether he thought it possible that France would be invaded and he replied that a French General had assured one of his friends that the Maginot Line could not be broken. No one had realised how easy it would be for Hitler to walk round through Belgium. When this happened the Works was quickly occupied. Akers managed to escape with the wages which financed his way back to England but Hague, who had married a French girl, remained and was interned. Basil and Harry Gardiner got back to England before the Germans reached Paris. Hammond had already retired but Charles Lipscomb who also had a French wife and a young family made his way to the South West of France and eventually got out through Spain to South Africa. M. Marguet who had been the Commercial Manager was left in charge of the office and the Works charge hand, Mr Mahiev, was the Manager at Blanc Misseron under German direction.

As soon as possible after the war Mr Akers went back and as Basil Green and Lipscomb were both past retiring age Simon engaged Charles Larking, his fellow officer in North Africa. Hague was released from prison camp and carried on as Sales and Commercial Manager in the Paris office assisted by M Benoit.

As soon as the restrictions of war ended orders started coming in and the first problem was to get production going. When Akers got back to Blanc Misseron he found that the employees refused to work under Mr Mahiev because he had taken his orders from the Germans during the occupation and was a collaborateur. Although no such evidence was ever found against him and he had managed to keep the plant and machinery intact, the workforce could not be persuaded that he should stay.

Profits were ploughed back to deal with the modernisation required at the Works and Wakefield were determined that there should be closer contact than before the War. The French company's designs which went back to the pre-war days differed from those of Wakefield but over the next decade these differences were mostly eliminated.

Charles Larking did brilliantly as many of the Wakefield staff had looked down on the French Company and wouldn't accept Continental ideas and couldn't accept that an ex-Irish Guards Officer had something to offer. Charles had to cultivate relations with Greens' principal customers including boilermakers and officials of the Electricite de France, (EdF). After the war many of the larger American International companies were seeking to establish themselves in Europe, sending representatives to be based in Paris. With his knowledge of France and the French, Charles was able to advise them, making many American friends some of whom helped to improve Greens' business connections, not only in France but also internationally.

Whilst the EdF were mostly adopting American licences for power station boilers Greens were able to establish a good connection in the marine market. Foster Wheeler from London had been licensing French shipyards to build their designs of marine boilers which included the special Foster economiser. With facilities to make these at Blanc Misseron Greens were able to supply Foster Wheeler economisers as in the UK and other European countries.

In early 1955, as part of my preparation for a career in Greens I was sent to Blanc Misseron to work as a labourer in the foundry: a sharp contrast to life at Eton and my home in Wiltshire. Mr Hague was still managing the factory which started work at 7 am. I was boarded out with the family of an Avocat called Treca, in Valencienne leaving for the factory at 6.30 am each morning on a tram.

I politely asked M Hague why there was no canteen or washhouse for the workers and his reply amazed me:

"M Basil forbad it" he said. "M Basil believed that if you gave workers a space in which they could relax and have a chat it always led to trouble and expensive demands".

Having recast hundreds of broken fire-grates and other iron household appliances brought in by the workers, I was moved to the Paris office, in Rue d'Aguesseau next door to the British Church. Based in Paris I travelled all over France as a site labourer installing economisers for a year. I also spent time in the Design Office in Paris and was given a great deal of information and support by Charles Larking.

When Charles was promoted to the UK Board and left France in 1957 Harry Gardiner went over as General Manager. He was fluent in French and having been in Paris before the war was well known to executives there, who were delighted to welcome him back. But he took over at a most unfortunate time with the downturn in the capital goods trade cycle and with two keen French competitors the Company entered a period of losses. Looking ahead there was no prospect of improvement. It was therefore decided to make an approach to Comeconomiseur who had had a rather smaller share of the market than Greens but joined with Greens might become a very effective competitor against Pont a Mousson. Comeconomiseur was owned by Madame Guesnet, daughter of the company's founder. Her husband was on the selling and commercial side, Madame held the purse strings. Charles Larking made a preliminary approach to Guesnet with the suggestion to try and work out a merger in which Greens would like him to continue to play an active part. This led to a lunch on a hot day in the courtyard of the Ritz Hotel In Paris. Charles and Simon were entertaining the two Guesnets. Negotiations seemed to be going splendidly and the idea was generally acceptable. Then came the question of finance and the Guesnets were asked whether both sides might exchange their last five years' trading figures as the basis of further discussion. At this point Madame sat upright and said "C'est impossible, Monsieur Larking, Colonel Green desire me voir nue" and that was the end of negotiations.

Having failed with this merger Greens still felt that the French market was too small to stand three manufacturers and sounded out Pont a Mousson. They had the largest share in the cast-iron economiser and airheater business but they had no competitive designs in the high pressure or marine market. A different line had to be taken with them as in a merger Greens would have been a very small sprat in their large organisation. Consequently a licence agreement was agreed whereby manufacture in France ceased and they paid royalties and fees for the designs Greens were able to introduce. This worked out well for Greens as after closing Blanc Misseron and settling redundancy problems Greens were able to repatriate just over £400,000 and in the ensuing years received rather more in annual license fees than from previous average profits.

3 E Green & Son (SA) (PTY) Ltd

In South Africa, in the post war years the economiser business was to a large extent based around the sugar industry. The boilers were fired with bagasse (dried spent sugar cane) and required large economisers. The cast iron gill designs were admirably suitable and these were shipped out from Wakefield with the steel framework and casings often manufactured locally. There were the occasional power station contracts but since the only suitable design at that time was the plain steel tube Greens were not particularly competitive.

In the nineteen seventies there was a considerable market for power station equipment, but not surprisingly, there was a growing requirement that equipment be manufactured locally. There were two reasons for this: uncertainty about security of supply because of apartheid trade sanctions and a dire shortage of foreign currency.

By this time Greens welded gill designs were available and were perfect for the job, the problem was to manufacture them locally. A local entrepreneur offered to build us a new factory on a long term leasehold. This seemed an ideal solution; plans were drawn up and our Managing Director in SA lost no time in bidding for and winning the next power station contract before the factory had been even started. But our Afrikaans entrepreneur turned out to be a man of straw and was declared bankrupt. This news reached Wakefield without any prior warning. Although there was no shortage of capital in Wakefield to build our own factory there was reluctance to commit it to South Africa in the light of the severe currency restrictions. In the event there was little or no time to make alternative arrangements and the factory went ahead with funds from Wakefield. A plot of land was purchased in the town of Vereeniging some twenty five miles from Johannesburg and the new factory was built.

Two fin-welding machines were shipped out from Wakefield and were installed just in time to start production of the first unit. Other contracts were to follow in rapid succession and after two years the factory was doubled in size.

The apartheid trade restrictions brought about a very severe oil shortage in South Africa and this led to a new industry springing up manufacturing oil products from coal. The chemical process, originally developed in Germany, required large quantities of steam and therefore boilers and economisers. Once again the welded gill designs came into their own. It was most fortunate that the fall off in sugar industry business coincided with the rise in power station and oil from coal business.

As the new factory in South Africa was being built Wakefield was busily involved in the air cooler business. Having got the welded gill machines up and running in South Africa the market for air coolers was explored and because of the requirement of local manufacture it was found to be wide open. Contracts were obtained and the tubes were initially shipped from Wakefield until finning machines were imported from Tulsa Oklahoma and a second product was added to the new factory which was going from strength to strength.

4 Italy

In Italy there was substantial business during the years of industrial build-up prior to 1914, supplying industrial installations through the Italian boilermakers Franco Tosi. In the nineteen twenties three direct representatives were employed, two of whom retired by 1933 and one

Feruccio Casinghini, a remarkable character, was left in charge. He had
started as office boy/interpreter. He was given some technical instruction
by John Rylands and he soon showed himself to be a very neat and
accomplished project draughtsman.

By 1935 the taxation policy of the Italian Government made it
advisable to form a company which we called S A Economizatori
Italiana Green. Casinghini was pressing for a Works to be set up in Italy
but this was resisted. Nevertheless Casinghini did lease a Works in his
own name and acquired some machinery so that led to disagreement and
suspicion of Casinghini's motives and when Mussolini invaded Albania
and the British Government brought in sanctions against trade with Italy,
all relations were broken off and the Italian company was wound up.

Soon after the War had ended in 1945 Casinghini turned up at
Wakefield. It appeared that he had successfully established his own
Works and business under the name of Casinghini Economizatori and
most of his products were labelled with Type Green. He started by
repaying the bad debt to Greens of some £1000.

His approach was that his business really belonged to Greens and he
wanted them to buy it. This was declined and it became obvious that the
purpose of his visit was to ascertain what changed and developments
had taken place in Wakefield. With the war commitments there had not
been many although Greens were by this time well established in the
marine market in conjunction with Foster Wheeler. Casinghini had set up
a production line in his own Works for making the elements required but
he had a very small market as the Italian boilermakers were
manufacturing their own economisers for power stations. He was,
therefore, most interested in Greens marine development and as Greens,
under their agreement with Foster Wheeler, had the right to supply in
Italy it was arranged that Casinghini should manufacture economisers
under licence to work in conjunction with steam boilers on ships.

The Managing Director of Foster Wheeler Ltd in London had heard
stories about Casinghini before the war and said that he wanted Greens
to be entirely responsible for the collection of licence fees from him
which were to be shared between Foster Wheeler and Greens. As Foster
Wheeler licenced most of the leading Italian shipyards to build their
boilers, a large number of orders for their economisers were passed to
Casinghini in the ensuing years. As time went on the payment of fees
became slower and slower and often with frantic pleas for a reduction in
rate backed by various excuses. Foster Wheeler had a complete record
of all the boilers supplied ender licence and, therefore, knew exactly the
number and size of all economisers that Casinghini had made so it was

difficult for him to evade the issue. Nevertheless there were countless arguments, correspondence and visits.

Casinghini had a number of developments of his own and no doubt he wished Greens would take licenses from him which would offset his marine economiser debts. There were two of his products in which Greens expressed an interest. First, Tankerheat for which he had adapted the Foster tube construction for an arrangement in the bottom of oil tankers in order to heat the oil to make it flow better when it was pumped out of the tanks. Second, he was again using the Foster tube for a heat exchanger to provide hot water and steam services for diesel propelled ships by recovering waste heat from the diesel engines. This he called a Diesecon which was not a novel name as it had been used and tried by Wakefield with vertical economisers for application with diesel engines on land in about 1911. There was still a good deal of work to be done in marketing and selling this idea for marine use and Wakefield would obviously have to make a contribution to the future development. It could not be readily agreed that this was entirely a Casinghini product and a more lenient view might have been taken if Feruccio had been more co-operative with the marine economiser dues. He had also made a grave mistake by increasing his prices to the Italian shipyards to whom he supplied the marine economisers to an extent where the price per ton looked absurd. Many objections were raised by customers back to Foster Wheeler who in their turn rightly turned to Greens for an explanation who could only conclude that Casinghini was taking an imprudent advantage of this tied, competition free business. But eventually the Ansaldo shipyard would stand no more and in spite of strong protests from Foster Wheeler insisted on purchasing identical economiser elements from a firm named Rizzi. The proprietor of this name had been a draughtsman with Casinghini and had left with all his experience to set up in competition. In these circumstances, Foster Wheeler and Greens were left with a very weak argument and they both felt extremely badly let down by Casinghini.

Finally, no reciprocal arrangements with Casinghini on Diesecon or Tankerheat could be agreed until he had paid all license fees up to date. Set time limits for settlement were not kept and so their training relationship ended. This was sad and a bad thing for both parties. In the coming years Wakefield developed an extremely good connection by the sale of Diesecons from which Casinghini might well have profited. On the other side, Casinghini was a resourceful and progressive thinker and Wakefield might well have developed more of his ideas if it had not been for a reluctance by the Greens engineering staff to accept the ideas of this Italian friend.

5 Germany

In 1869 Greens first direct representative was appointed and a selling organisation was built up in Cologne where George Usher, the junior member of staff, was promoted by Frank Green on one of his rare visits, to be an outdoor salesman using the firm's motorbike.

In 1911 a subsidiary company E Green & Sons GmbH was formed in Gelsenkinchen. A factory, fitted with cranes, specialist machines and suitable railway sidings was nearing completion at the end of the summer of 1914 when war broke out. In 1919 a successful claim for £90,000 was paid by German Government and attempts were made to resume trade but in 1933 the decision was made to discontinue representation.

Pictures Index

Ten of the images are reproduced from 'Waste Not'. The picture on page 28 is reproduced from a National Trust postcard. Other pictures are from Stan Jewson's and Green family archives.

Alphabetical Index

GORDON Betts – Greens Youngest Foreman

Extract from the Appreciation at his funeral in Wakefield Cathedral in October 2001

By Mike Swift

An only child, Gordon was born in Normanton but his family soon moved to Wakefield where he became a chorister in this Cathedral, rejoicing in its music and ceremony and aspiring to its exactingly high standards.

His working life began with an engineering apprenticeship with E Green & Sons in this city. This exposure to, and interaction with a diverse group of people in this large factory made a great impression on Gordon. In particular it helped develop his incisive skill at observing people – their characteristics and idiosyncrasies being studied, compared and later recalled with the proficiency of a top-class comedian or character actor.

Gordon was also an accomplished musician. He played piano but his enthusiasm for the big bands of the day caused him to take up the drums. His dexterity on this instrument was honed in the dance bands of the 1950s and later backing the Kettlethorpe Trio during the great days of this local club. Though Gordon was modest about his musical accomplishments we all knew that even a 'top of the bill' artist depended on Gordon's skill and timing to achieve the right impact.

At Greens Gordon progressed to become the youngest foreman ever appointed by Greens and took charge of the large Fabrication Shop. Former draughtsmen still recall his visits to their office, demanding drawings for more fabrications to satisfy what he described as his insatiable monster.

Gordon's remarkable character and appreciation of personal relations endeared him to everyone; especially those tempted to occupy the confessional chair beside his desk. Here he dispensed worldly advice, earthy wisdom and endless wit. He also bestowed well-chosen nicknames on his colleagues and business associates based on an acute observation of their personal characteristics. These often described the person so accurately as to be remembered long after their names had been forgotten. But Gordon's humour was always benevolent and his best jokes usually concerned himself.

It is these departed merits that we, his colleagues and friends, will miss the most